Astrology & Health

Sheila Geddes, D.F.Astrol.S., has been a practising astrologer for many years. She has been Secretary to the British Faculty of Astrological Studies, the recognised examining body for astrologers all over the world, and has taught and set examination papers for them, as well as lectured widely on all aspects of astrology.

Other titles by Sheila Geddes:
Self-Development With Astrology
The Art of Astrology

Astrology & Health

by

SHEILA GEDDES

foulsham

London • New York • Toronto • Sydney

foulsham
Yeovil Road, Slough, Berkshire, SL1 4JH

ISBN 0-572-01822-3

Printed in Great Britain, Cox & Wyman Ltd., Reading

CONTENTS

DEDICATION

For Alec

ACKNOWLEDGEMENTS

I wish to thank all the consultants who have given me interviews or allowed me to quote from their work. I also wish to thank Constance D. Leigh for vetting my section on Radionics and for other valuable help and advice.

AUTHOR'S NOTE

I am delighted that my publishers have agreed to reissue this book, as I have continually been asked for copies of *Astrology and Health* since it went out of print.

I make no apology for the fact that much of the material from the original book is repeated here, since the basics do not change, but much has happened on the complementary medicine scene in the last ten years and I welcome the opportunity to update and greatly expand the information.

Not the least of the changes is the extent to which the various therapies have been accepted by the general public, and increasingly by medical practitioners. It should now be possible to find therapists for all the treatments mentioned in this book.

INTRODUCTION

In 1964, when I first became a professional astrologer, I knew that my interest would lie chiefly in helping other people with their problems, so I also took some training in counselling.

The birth chart gives an insight into the psychological make-up of the person to whom the chart relates and it is easy for a trained astrologer to see what clients may be doing to cause their own difficulties.

I have written elsewhere* of other problems which may be overcome (if not solved) by an understanding of your own psychological traits, but in this book I shall deal specifically with health.

Twenty years before I became an astrologer, I married a man who is a born healer, and whose interests have been, for many years, in the field of alternative techniques.

We found that my skills both as an astrologer and as a counsellor gave us another valuable tool in helping his patients and also in keeping ourselves healthy.

Counselling is now recognised as being most valuable in the treatment of health problems, as so many of them are caused, or exacerbated, by bottling-up resentment, frustrations or anger which puts the whole body under tension or stress.

* *Self-Development with Astrology*

The Institute for Complementary Medicine now insists that all healers who wish to be recognised as professionals should have training in counselling, and the charities which have been founded to treat the whole person offer it as an essential part of therapy.

But there are, of course, many minor health problems which respond to one or more of the alternative therapies and some of these you can treat at home quite safely. Any problem which does not respond quickly to self-treatment should be referred to a qualified practitioner. Details of how to find them will be found in the Further Information section at the end of this book.

How to use the book

If you are predominantly a 'Fire' type, you should read the sections for all the Fire signs – Aries, Leo and Sagittarius, and similarly for the other triplicities. Earth signs are Taurus, Virgo and Capricorn. Air signs are Gemini, Libra and Aquarius and Water signs are Cancer, Scorpio and Pisces.

I hope that you will read through the descriptions of all the therapies so that you will be aware of the many treatments available to you today. Details of practitioners or associations from whom you can get further information are listed at the back of the book.

If you do not know your birth chart (apart from the Sun sign) and you have an illness, you should read the information for the sign which governs that part of the body. These are as follows:

ARIES   Head, cerebral system, adrenal glands

TAURUS   Neck, throat, eustachian tubes, thyroid gland, cervical vertebrae

GEMINI	Hands, arms, shoulders, lungs and nervous system
CANCER	Breasts, stomach, alimentary system
LEO	Heart, spine, cardiac system, gall bladder
VIRGO	Abdomen, intestines, visceral system
LIBRA	Lower back, kidneys, renal system
SCORPIO	Pelvis, sexual organs, generative system, prostate glands, rectum
SAGITTARIUS	Hips, thighs, liver, hepatic system
CAPRICORN	Knees, bones, teeth, skin, skeletal system
AQUARIUS	Ankles, shins, circulatory system
PISCES	Feet, duodenum, pituitary gland.

Even those who know their zodiacal make-up will have certain indicators in the birth chart which may indicate a health weakness not connected with their general type. For example, I am primarily a 'Water/Earth' type, but I also have a strong Mars in Aries and sometimes have eye troubles (which would come under the Aries rulership of the head). In such a case, I would look for an Aries remedy. The index gives a quick reference for this.

Attitude to health

Your attitude to your own health and the treatment of disorders is all-important. Most therapists know patients who expect to be cured after one treatment and who try a whole string of therapists of various types without giving any treatment a chance to work. These are usually people who expect the therapist to wave a magic wand and seem quite unaware that they can (and should) contribute to their own recovery, by taking an intelligent interest in getting to the cause of the trouble and then making sure that they do not aggravate it. If a therapist diagnoses the prime cause of an illness as wrong diet it is useless for the patient to change the therapy without changing the diet.

If you read with this understanding, you will be able to prevent the forms of disease to which your constitution (admirably shown by your birth chart) predisposes you. In addition, an understanding of your own psychological make-up will enable you to adjust your regime to one which is just right for you and which will ensure a long, healthy and happy life.

PSYCHOLOGICAL CAUSES
OF ILLNESS

Psychology As Revealed by the Elements

There will be a precise description of the psychology of each
of the zodiacal pattern types under the appropriate sign, but
we can recognise a general pattern, even from the Elements
(sometimes called 'Triplicities').

The Fire types often have abundant energy and vitality, and
they tend to get trapped into situations where they spend that
energy recklessly. The result, in terms of ill-health, can be
accidents, fever or over-activity of the vital organs.

Earth types, being practical and 'fixed', tend to contract the
ailments associated with cold and rigidity, often with inhibition of movement.

The lungs and nerves are emphasised in the Air types.
Restlessness is common, with appropriate nervous ailments.
These people tend to be easily upset by quarrels or uncongenial
conditions, and can induce psychosomatic illnesses to avoid
an unpleasant situation.

Water types are emotional, sensitive and sympathetic, so
that they become open to worry or suspicion. They can also
be fearful and imaginative to the extent of contracting mental
troubles.

The 'Triggers' for Ill-health

There are perhaps a dozen causes of ill-health, some of which would appear to be unavoidable. They include shock, accidents and infection, though even these can be minimised by the knowledge that one is prone to them, if the necessary precautions are then taken. Others are completely avoidable and these include boredom, self-centredness, resentment, frustration, dread (of old age, loneliness, of the unknown, etc.) and depletion caused by an unhealthy regime. The latter may include smoking, wrong diet or overactivity of any kind, and of course, actual abuse of the body.

Psychosomatic Illness

It has to be recognised that a person who is ill often has a vested interest, in staying that way. I have already mentioned one cause – to avoid unpleasant situations. Others which are well recognised by the medical profession include: to avoid making decisions, fear of failure ('If I'm not well enough to take the examination, I can't fail it'), to get attention (and, therefore, avoid being lonely), to provide proof of love ('my husband will do anything for me'), to keep another person subservient ('smother-love'). Resentment often manifests as a power complex. We have all heard of the ailing mother who bosses the whole family as they all run around after her because she is ill.

Years ago, I spent a sleepless night (and was unable to go to work the next day) having coped with an unstable woman who deliberately took alcohol, knowing that it was forbidden when she was taking certain drugs. The result was a dreadful scene during which she attacked my husband and I and insisted on telephoning her boss, after midnight, in order to abuse him. We quietened her down and put her to bed and she enjoyed a good night's sleep. I shall never forget her triumphant smile the next morning as she realised what the effect had been on me. It said so clearly 'Look what I have been able to do to you.' Needless to say, no-one has been able to do it since.

Another example of a psychosomatic illness occurred with a young man who complained of excessive lassitude and pains in his legs. My husband, finding nothing physically wrong with him, handed him over to me. A short session with Gestalt techniques convinced me that there was a deep-seated psychological cause, and as I was unable to undertake a prolonged course with him, I arranged for him to make a contract with another therapist. Her diagnosis agreed with mine. He was the son of a brilliant man, and his father expected great things of him which were not within his power to give. His illness had been induced to provide an excuse (and to avoid failure). It was, no doubt, very real to him, but was, nevertheless, a classic case of someone playing the game which Eric Berne called 'Wooden Leg',* ('What can you expect of a man with a wooden leg?').

Some illnesses are caused by a desire, perhaps I should say a compulsion, to please others. Very often, this is the parents, even though they may no longer be alive. Most people carry 'parent messages' all through their lives and try to please 'the parent in the head'. They expect their lives to be a pattern of their mother's (if a woman) or their father's (if a man).

A lady came to see my husband because she was convinced that she could not walk without support. Again, he could find no physical cause and suspected that this was a psychosomatic illness. I began questioning her and said I would like to set up her birth chart. She agreed and I asked her for her birth date. The day and the month were given readily – 'and the year?' I asked. She looked at me for a long moment and then said 'How old do you think I am?' 'I've no idea', I replied, 'but I'm 56, if it makes any difference.' 'I'm sixty', she said in a tone

* *Games People Play* by Eric Berne, M.D.

which indicated that that was a very serious age to be. We then started on the family history and it emerged that her mother had died at the age of 59. I could already see why she thought 60 was an advanced age. Then I asked her 'Have you always been highly-strung?' 'Yes,' she said, 'when I was a child, my mother used to say that I should not get so tense, as she had had a friend who was so nervous that eventually she was unable to walk.' The picture was now so very clear to me, but all my efforts to get her to see *what she was doing to herself* failed. As I never saw her again (having got too near to the truth) I can only assume that she was trying to please the 'parent in her head' by following her mother – not having been able to die at 59, she was willing herself to become ill, and, since she did not want to see what she was doing, it is likely that she also had the ulterior motive of keeping her husband constantly by her side.

Many people think that if a doctor tells them that they have a psychosomatic illness, he is saying, 'You are imagining it'. This is not so. It is definitely a physical illness caused by the things which we do to ourselves. If a muscle is held under tension for any length of time, it will soon start to ache, and if we take no notice of the pain and persist in holding it tense we will eventually be unable to move it. Rigidity has set in. Yet we constantly hold ourselves under tension – 'bottling up' emotions, working flat out for long periods, pushing ourselves beyond our capabilities – these can all result in illnesses which have a psychological cause and hence are known as psychosomatic.

We have analysed our records of the many cases of agoraphobia and find that these are often connected with the marriage partner. About half the cases occurred where the partners were not happy and the agoraphobic one appears to have withdrawn from the world rather than cope with the situation in any of the more obvious ways. The result was often that the other partner went out by themselves, thus having the desired effect as far as the agoraphobic was concerned. In at least two cases, the agoraphobia occurred when a loved partner was missing and was completely cured in one of the cases when he returned permanently, and in the other case when the women became pregnant on one of his short leaves at home.

Arthritis would appear to be a purely physical ailment, but it has been noticeable in our cases, that many of the arthritics do not seem to have the willpower or initiative to continue with healing sessions as soon as they begin to show improvement.

One card carries the cryptic message to us 'this patient is very self-orientated. She straightens up when she forgets herself', and another says 'very self-orientated not enough outlets'. One who improved tremendously and said that she wanted to get a job never got round to getting one, and when urged by her husband to come back to us for general upliftment agreed to do so, but, in fact, never did. She had the added burden of an ageing and dominating mother living with her. This type of tension often seems to trigger off arthritis and related illnesses.

Bronchitis was always known as 'the English disease' and it is still prevalent, whereas the related illness, tuberculosis, has decreased greatly. The modern diseases of the Western World are cancer and heart trouble (together with arthritis) – all of these appear to be related to tension and are symptomatic of the world in which we live. Cardiac difficulties are more likely to be experienced by the Fire types (those who push their tensions into overwork) while cancer is more likely in those who do not release tensions at all (notably Earth types). Cancer is a strange disease as it has no single cause. It is an alteration in the behaviour of the cells of the body for no obvious medical reason. Nevertheless, over many years of experience, we have had many cases of cancers which have been completely cured by healing. It is almost as if people attracted it to themselves, and, having accepted the assurance that it can be cured, they 'throw it off' easily. Zipporah Dobyns (Pottinger) has cited the case of a patient who got cancer several times and each time decided to deal with it herself. Her method was to go away by herself and lie in the sun, relax and forgive everyone who she felt might have harmed her. She also recognised that her grown-up children were quite capable of managing their own lives and resolved that she would leave them to do so in future and not spend her time worrying about them. Her self-treatment worked each time without any medical aid. This certainly bears out our own experience. We believe that a large number of cancers are psychosomatic and they have certainly proved some of the easiest cases to cure. (See also details of the Cancer Help Centre on page 157.) Further information on heart troubles and arthritis is also given later (see index).

TYPES OF TREATMENT

Alternative Medicine

Just as each zodiacal type is more prone to some illnesses than to others, so each will react more quickly to some types of treatment than others. There are now many types of alternative medicines and therapies widely available and I have provided a list of the sources of further information for those mentioned here at the back of this book. Methods where it is safe to treat yourself have been described in detail.

Orthodox, or allopathic, medicine is largely drug-based and most general practitioners are too overburdened with patients to look for causes of illness. All they can do is to treat the symptoms – a fact which many of them recognise and deplore.

One of the most encouraging features of the last ten years (since I wrote the original edition of *Astrology and Health*) is the extent to which more and more doctors are open to the ideas originated by the so-called 'fringe' practitioners and are increasingly becoming qualified in one or more of the therapies themselves.

I wrote in that book 'Nobody is more aware of the dangers of recognising the fringe medicines than the fringe practitioner … who … is only too well aware that there are many practising (since there is no law to stop them) with very little skill, knowledge or technique to recommend them.' A year after the book was published, The Institute for Complementary

Medicine realised that EEC regulations were likely to supersede the Common Law of the UK, and they started a registration scheme for all practitioners who worked to agreed standards. Courses leading to degree, diploma or certificate level are now available and are investigated by external examiners.

So successful has the research and planning been that the Institute now publishes the British Register of Complementary Practitioners. This has been welcomed by The British Medical Association, General Medical Council and the general public. The Institute answers over 50,000 enquiries each year.

The ICM supplies information to local authorities, MPs and the media. Over 100 training organisations are associated with the Institute and they hope to establish a training college during the next decade.

Contact Healing

Healing by the laying-on of hands (sometimes called spiritual healing or more commonly, but erroneously 'faith healing') has proved itself to be a valuable form of alternative treatment, often succeeding in cases which have been given up by orthodox medicine. Its basis is still not understood. Many healers, who are also spiritualists, believe that 'spirit doctors' work through them. Others, often called 'magnetic healers', believe that they heal through their own magnetic powers. These healers certainly do use something of themselves, as they become depleted after healing sessions. In his book *The Occult*, Colin Wilson suggests that some, at least, of the documented cases of healing have been the result of strong suggestion by the healer. 'Colonel Olcott ... found that using his thaumaturgic power was like riding a bicycle, a matter of confidence and practice. The Colonel believed; the sufferers believed; and cures were affected by the dozen.' He admits, however, that this explanation will not hold up for the cures affecting animals. It is for this reason that I described the term 'faith healing' as erroneous. Young children and animals do not have faith, yet there have been remarkable cures of both. What is certain is that healing will not work unless the patient is open-minded and willing to be cured. A complete sceptic who is willing the healer to fail will put up a barrier in his mind which will adequately prevent any healing reaching him.

Alec Geddes, who was born with the healing gift, describes it as follows:

When healing starts I am aware of power flowing in between my shoulder blades, down my arms and out through my fingers. I never feel depleted after healing. Why should I? It is not me that supplies the power. I am only a cable plugged into a power point. In fact, some of the healing seems to 'rub off' on me, as I usually have plenty of energy and tend to shake off any infections I may pick up in a much shorter time than the average person. I do not require a patient to have faith in me, or in any particular religion, but I am not allowed to override the patient's own will, so if he does not wish to be well, I cannot help him. The patient must also be willing to help himself. If I tell him he must cut out smoking, and that I will help him to do this, but he does not even try, then I don't want to know him. I am not in the business of doing for people what they should do for themselves. I would not describe myself as a Spiritualist, though I agree with their philosophy, but I do believe that I am overshadowed by other helping entities, and I am able to distinguish between them, so that I can often tell which one is working with me. I do not believe that I have a 'direct line' to God, or that it is up to me to decide who will be cured, but I usually know as soon as I see people whether, or not, I can help them.

Among the remarkable cures achieved through him have been that of a Highland bull who was thought by the veterinary doctors to be suffering from leukaemia; the removal of a brain tumour from a dog (this was dissolved through the eye duct) and the complete cure of a man who was discharged from HM Forces over thirty years ago with spinal trouble. He was just managing to walk with the aid of two sticks when he began to come for treatment. His story is also remarkable as it shows the necessity for the patient to be in the right frame of mind. For months he made no progress, and Alec Geddes stopped the treatment saying, 'There is something wrong here. Either I am not doing my job properly, or you are not accepting this.' After some weeks, the patient asked to start the treatment again, explaining that he came from a family of medical people and had found it difficult to believe that anything could result from this type of healing, but he was now prepared to be more positive about it. When treatment commenced again, the results were almost immediate. The ankle (which had been locked for thirty years) began to move, then the spine started to loosen up. First one crutch and then the other was discarded.

It was a great joy, after a few weeks more, to see him come striding up the path to the house. He continued to work until the normal retirement age, though he had been a candidate for early retirement when he first came to us. He told us that one by-product of the healing had been that Alec had taught him to relax (and to take a relaxed attitude about things he could not change) so that he no longer fretted and fumed when caught in a traffic hold-up. Considering the amount of illness caused by just such tension, it was a 'by-product' well worth having.

Radionics and Dowsing

Another form of treatment which has much in common with healing is Radionics, since it, too, is inexplicable in terms of modern science. It derives from dowsing (radiesthesia) and indeed, good dowsers can cut out the aid of the radionic diagnostic 'box' and get their answers direct from the pendulum.

Many people are able to dowse – perhaps half of us. I have had the experience of holding metal rods and feel them turn round in my hands as I approached a pool of water. Anyone who can do this can learn to use a pendulum, which is simply a weight at the end of a string or cord. Almost any material can be used to make it, from a cotton reel on a piece of string to a jewel on a chain. This will answer any question which can be answered by 'yes' or 'no'. For most people the 'positive' is a clockwise swing, with a 'negative' going anti-clockwise. This does not follow for everyone and you can determine you own positive and negative in the following way. If you are right-handed, hold the pendulum in your right hand, and let it swing over the extended first finger of the left hand. This is the 'positive' finger, and the direction of the swing gives the positive answer for you, personally. The next one – the middle finger – is negative and you can get your negative swing from it.

One idea behind dowsing is that you have a 'higher mind' which can find out anything there is to know and by concentrating on the pendulum you tune in to that higher mind, which will give you the answer to your questions. It is necessary to keep the conscious mind neutral, which is to say that you must not be concerned with the answer to your question. Anything highly personal which mattered enormously to you would allow the emotions to interfere with the working of the pendulum. It is also necessary to work with it regularly for at least a year (to establish a rapport with it) before you can begin to have confidence in it.

I have seen Dr Arthur Bailey diagnose and prescribe for patients solely by using the pendulum. He asked it, 'Which remedy shall I use?' then held it over a range of them until he got a positive reaction from one or more. Then he asked, in turn, 'What is the dose?', 'How many times a day?' and 'How long for?' getting his answers in little more time that it has taken me to describe.

Some radionics boxes combine both diagnosis and treatment. In other cases, a separate box is used for each process. Something from the patient's body – a lock of hair, nail-parings, a spot of blood – is used as a 'witness', in radionic parlance, and placed in the diagnostic box. It has dials which can be set to diagnose the patient's illness but this is a long, slow process and most good practitioners will rely on the pendulum for diagnosis. It is not always essential to place a witness in the diagnostic box, but it is essential for treatment. This is given by setting the dials on the box to 'broadcast' the remedy indicated to the patient or to counteract the disease. No electricity is used and there is no scientific explanation as to why the 'black box' should work. It is suggested that the treatment reaches the patient by the currents passing through the energy fields all about us, in the same way that electrical currents are present, but remain undetected, unless we have a receiver and transmitter both tuned to the correct wave length.

In his book *Mysteries*, Colin Wilson tells of the work of T.C. Lethbridge who discovered the 'rates' for various objects by experimenting with pendulums of different lengths – for instance, at a length of twenty-two inches the pendulum went positive for silver and lead. He tested many different substances, including foods, milk, alcohol – even diamonds. Armed with the knowledge that the rate for truffles was seventeen inches, he even succeeded in finding a rare type of truffle in a wood.

It is this knowledge of the rates of different remedies which is used by the radionics practitioner to set the correct rate on the dial of the box and so broadcast it to the patient.

This is another form of treatment which will be applicable to all the zodiacal types, though it is probably more effective for patients who have some belief in it, or who are, at least, open-minded.

Colour and Sound Therapies

'The future of medicine lies in light and sound', said the great medium and healer, Edgar Cayce.

Both of these therapies like radionics, are related to the invisible wave forms in the ether around us, and practitioners believe that their healing is borne on these wave currents to the patient concerned. Unlike radionics, both colour and sound treatments are given in the presence of the patient. The colour is beamed at the affected area of the body by means of a lamp with coloured slides (and sometimes using a radionics box as well) and the sound is transmitted by means of an applicator which is directly applied to the body. In both therapies the idea of the 'whole' (meaning both 'complete' and 'wholesome' or healthy) becoming out of balance or out of harmony is described in similar ways.

In colour healing it is alleged that the body requires the energy of the Sun in its pure form in order to stay healthy and this comprises the whole spectrum of light which can be divided into the colours we see – red, orange, yellow, green, blue, indigo and violet. Imbalances in the body imply a deficiency of one or more colours and can be corrected by transmitting the ones required direct to the patient.

Sound therapists recognise that all atoms, including those making up cells and organs, are in a state of continuous vibration which, therefore, send out energy – two forms of which are light and sound. If the energy pattern changes, the frequency will change and produce a break-up into smaller units.

Peter Guy Manners, in his book *The Sound of Healing* describes the process as follows:

Each vibrating body is emitting a sound corresponding to its frequency ... These sounds coming from every part of the body, combine to give the sound characteristic of the whole body ... in a healthy body the chord is complete and harmonious. When disease breaks into an organ its note becomes discordant and the harmony is upset. The curative process is intended to restore the note to its original purity and then the body is harmonious once more.

Treatment given at his clinic has been mainly concerned with tissues and bones and it has been successful for arthritis, rheumatoid, fibrositis, fractures and bone disorders and muscular conditions (especially where nerves are involved).

As in so many cases, these conditions can be relieved, but where the cause of the condition is of psychosomatic origin, the cause has to be treated if a complete cure is to be achieved.

Mrs Alice Howard, who is a homoeopath, radionics practitioner and colour therapist, gives the following information with regard to the colours used in healing.

RED   stimulates and activates the nerves and the blood; releases adrenalin and stimulates the sensory nerves; vitalises the physical body, but must be used with caution as it can over stimulate.

              Red is contra-indicated in inflammatory conditions and emotional disturbances. Red should never be used alone but must be followed by green or blue.

ORANGE   is a combination of red and yellow; can be tolerated longer than red; is antiseptic in action and good for the treatment of cramps and spasms; aids the calcium metabolism and strengthens the lungs, the pancreas and the spleen; raises the pulse rate but not the blood pressure. The emotions become enlivened and general well-being can be experienced.

YELLOW   activates the motor nerves and creates energy in the muscles; works favourably on the digestion, but when used too long might cause diarrhoea, as it stimulates the flow of bile; gets rid of intestinal parasites; activates the lymph. Yellow is the colour of the intellect.

Yellow is contra-indicated in inflammatory states, delirium, diarrhoea, fever, over-excitement and palpitation of the heart.

GREEN   dilates the capillaries and creates a sensation of warmth; relieves tension, but should not be used too long; is a pituitary gland stimulant and a muscle tissue builder.

BLUE   increases the metabolism; promotes suppuration; heals burns. Blue is the colour of intuition and of higher mental faculties.

Blue is contra-indicated in the treatment of gout, hypertension, muscle contractions, chronic rheumatism and tachycardia (rapid heart beat).

INDIGO   depresses the motor nerves and the lymphatics as well as the cardiac system; purifies the blood and is a leucocyte builder.

VIOLET   maintains the potassium balance in the body; stops the growth of tumours; controls excess hunger.

There are also combinations of colours to give the shades of lemon, purple, scarlet, magenta, turquoise and pink.

LEMON   is a combination of light yellow and light green; is a laxative; is good for some skin complaints; is a cerebral stimulant. Yellow is anti-acid.

PURPLE   is a combination of more blue than red; has an analgesic property; suppresses malaria.

SCARLET   is a combination of more red than blue; stimulates the kidneys and the sexual mechanism.

MAGENTA   is a combination of red and violet; energises the adrenal glands and the action of the heart.

TURQUOISE   is a combination of blue and green; is good for some skin disorders; helps to clear up sinusitis.

PINK   is a combination of red and white; works favourably on the emotions.

Health depends on the proper balance of energy within the body. Light or colour is energy in a form which can be readily used to correct imbalance, thus restoring the body to health.

Astrologers will see many connections with harmonics, and with the zodiacal signs and the planets. However, I do not wish to make specific recommendations as to which astrological type will respond most readily to these therapies. All who are prepared to accept them with open minds are likely to experience the benefit. I am impressed by the fact that Alice Howard, with all her qualifications and thirty-five years of experience (which include eighteen years with a medical doctor), now chooses to concentrate solely on colour therapy.

Massage – Therapy and Treatment

Like some of the other techniques, massage can be used to invigorate or relax the body, or it can be used as a remedy for aches and pains, pulled muscles and even some deeper troubles.

Massage is a natural reaction to a hurt, from 'Mummy will rub it better' which we remember from childhood, to the soothing stroking of the forehead to relieve Grandma's headache. It follows that any of us can learn to do massage, though deep treatments are only for the experts.

At its simplest, it is a gentle stroking all over the body using oil as a lubricant. We recommend soya oil which is cheap and easily obtainable, and suits most people's skins, but any vegetable or nut oil will do and you will quickly get to know your own favourites. Talcum powder can be used on anyone who does not like oil, but it is not so easy to use, as you need to apply it more often and it is not so friction-free as oil.

Most people find massage an enjoyable experience and it is an ideal way to help people to relax. When we are tense, we automatically tighten up our muscles and massage loosens them again. Often we do not realise what we are doing and it is a common experience in all relaxation techniques to discover that a group of muscles is being held under tension even though the patient thought that they were completely relaxed. The relief of 'letting go' is enormous. Even in conditions of pain the 'giving way' to the pain and letting it flow through you – accepting it – can help to relieve it more than trying to keep it at bay by tensing against it. What is true of a physical condition is also true of an emotional one, and it is for this reason that emotional tension can often break down during massage (or healing particularly) and the patient may find relief in a good weep. These are 'healing waters' and should never be inhibited.

A really tight, bunched or pulled muscle needs deep massage and this *should not be given by the layman*. There is an art to knowing at what stage one can go deeper, as well as a science of understanding the nature and function of the muscle, and, as in all art, some practitioners are more skilled than others.

The movements which make a massage stimulating rather than relaxing are also better left to the expert, though a vigorous rub-down with oil followed by a rough towelling can be safely undertaken by everyone. There are several good books showing the various massage techniques. The booklist in the appendix will give you some guidance.

As regards the zodiacal types, the art of giving massage belongs particularly to those who wish to help others in a caring way. The use of hands directly on to the body of another person conveys sympathy and protectiveness and is well expressed by the Cancer subject and the Water signs generally. (I may add, that if the Cancer type is also a good cook who makes her own bread, she has already learned the kneading movement which is useful for breaking down fatty deposits in the body!) Gemini and Virgo types, who are good with their hands, also make good masseurs, provided they have enough intuition and feeling to empathise with the patient's needs.

The use of massage between lovers can help frigidity and temporary impotence, and it is perhaps not surprising that the people who enjoy massage the most are the Taureans and Scorpions. The Taureans, with their deep sensuality, simply enjoy the luxurious feeling of being pampered, especially if the massage is done with sweet-smelling oils (see Aromatherapy) and the same is true of Librans, though they may find it more difficult to relax at first. The Scorpion enjoys a stimulating massage, though he often needs a relaxing one more and the same is true of all the Fire Signs, especially the Arien.

Aquarius and Capricorn types are the ones who are most likely to be resistant to the idea of massage, though they are the people who could benefit greatly from it, as it helps them to overcome their inhibitions about getting close to other people. It has been said that the therapy you are most resistant to is the one you most need and it would certainly appear to be true in this case.

As with all the treatments, so with massage: certain techniques are safe for the layman, but damaged muscles and tissue must be left to the expert, and no part of the body should be touched by the layman where actual pain is being experienced, for whatever reason. I have had cause to be grateful, on more than one occasion, for massage techniques which have relieved gastric pains, by working on the colon. At such a time the whole stomach is sensitive and only the sure knowledge that my husband knew what he was doing and could relieve the pain would have induced me to let him touch those flaring nerves. Obviously then, such techniques must be left to those who are qualified to deal with them.

Do not let this caveat prevent you from experiencing the pleasure and sense of well-being that can come from both giving and receiving massage, however. It has a lot to offer to everyone, even on a superficial level.

Aromatherapy

The use of essential oils in foods and medicines is widely accepted. We could mention several which will be fully described under 'Herbs' – rosemary, lavender, bergamot and so on – and we are all familiar with orange and lemon essence for flavourings. Their use in cosmetics, particularly perfumes, is also well known, but with a few exceptions, we have generally considered them as being useful only for their agreeable odour.

The recent fashion for using more natural ingredients has led to a rash of cosmetics appearing on the market, widely advertised to contain peach oil, avocado oil, cucumber oil – and indeed the oils from practically every plant that grows. It is a moot point whether these do half as much good on the skin as some of them do if taken internally, but there is no doubt that essences do penetrate the skin, and also that their odours have a direct effect on us.

It is certain that the ancient Greeks, Romans, Egyptians and Jews used them widely and were aware of their many applications, for medicines, for preservatives and to maintain health, and it will be a great gain to our own era if the pursuit of the 'natural' increases our own knowledge of them.

Psychological and Physiological attributes of Essential Oils

All the oils have affinities with the mind and emotions and also with different parts of the body. There are those that work physically (healing direct) and those that work psychologically through the emotions (through the sense of smell) and these also work as preventative medicine.

Carrier oils

Recommended are peach kernel, apricot kernel, almond or soya oil. For massage, do not add more than six drops of any essential oil to 15 ml of carrier oil and don't blend more than four essential oils.

For adding to a bath use not more than six drops of any oil and only two or three drops of anything you are not sure of, and only the one essential oil. These oils can be obtained from St Clair Aromatics, 206 Kneller Road, Twickenham, Middlesex TW2 7EF.

The Oils which are Most Useful

Bergamot

Dispels gloom, takes the heat out of arguments and hostility by lightening the atmosphere. Helps with mental and psychological states, especially resentment. Also in dealing with weight problems caused by resentment, whether obesity (eating to compensate) or anorexia. It is a powerful antiseptic and is anti-viral. It relates to the uro-genital tract and is useful for cystitis or herpes.

It takes the discomfort out of chicken pox and is useful for shingles. *Direct sunlight on skin which is impregnated with bergamot oil can cause a rash*. Use two or three drops to 15 ml carrier oil.

Rosemary

This is a head oil, working directly on the brain. It is good for loss of memory, poor concentration and mental apathy, and is my favourite for waking my brain up in the morning or before giving a lecture. It is warming, cleansing and clearing and it stimulates the central nervous system. On a psychological level it helps loneliness, introversion and melancholy. It is indicated if the sensory nerves are affected, for example, loss of smell, poor vision, speech impairment and temporary paralysis. *Do not use as a single oil on anyone who is delicate*.

TYPES OF TREATMENT

Geranium

This is a good stabiliser for those who are feeling irrational and is indicated where humour would help. It stimulates and balances the adrenal cortex and the lymphatic system, so helps with elimination problems. It is a friendly oil and I use it in most massage mixtures, though I find it too heavy to use on its own.

Rose

Most people react well to this oil. It is soothing, cleansing, gently uplifting and cosseting. It helps to restore confidence and overcome shyness. It is particularly indicated in sadness caused by the breakup of a relationship. It is beneficial to female sexuality on both physical and emotional levels and helps insecurity in this area, for example, feelings of un-desirability, frigidity, impotence. It is an excellent tonic and is good in pregnancy, after birth or miscarriage and for meno-pausal symptoms. Clary sage and sandalwood are the equiv-alent for men's sexual problems.

Lavender

This is the most versatile of oils. Its therapeutic range is huge. It brings the body and mind into balance and calms the heart. It is indicated for nervous crises, hysteria, acute anxiety, etc. It was not for nothing that the ladies of former days had lavender water in their vinaigrettes to ward off their fainting fits! It induces sleep and it is a sedative, but it also helps fatigue and debility. Psychologically it helps moods which swing widely, paranoia and suspicion or lack of trust. It is analgesic, antiseptic and anti-spasmodic. It is a good nervine and is indicated for epilepsy, and, of course, fainting. It helps head-aches, migraines and rheumatism. It is also useful during childbirth. It helps anyone in acute pain, whether emotional or physical. It is an oil which may be applied undiluted to the

33

skin as an *immediate* treatment for burns and for spots on the skin. *This is the only oil which can be used undiluted.*

Frankincense

This has the ability to calm and to slow the breathing, hence its use for meditation. It is good to stimulate thought unhindered by the emotions. It promotes a spiritual outlook and detachment from worldly cares. It helps people who tend to dwell in the past. It is useful for hypnosis. It helps those who are 'down' or have feelings of inferiority and a lack of self worth. It also helps very materialistic people who may be compensating for these feelings. It is indicated in cases of fanaticism, religious conflict and unpleasant situations. You could say that it wards off 'the evil eye'. On a more mundane level it is generally revitalising and is good for the lungs, respiration, digestion and asthma. It is a very good skin-care oil. It is elevating and helps to expand the consciousness.

Clary Sage

This is both euphoric and relaxing! It is also an aphrodisiac and is recommended for couples going through a difficult time (for whatever reason). It promotes well-being and restores confidence. It is good for convalescence, debility and depression; also following bereavement and in any situation where there is necessity to change. It strengthens the willpower. It is indicated for kidney and stomach ailments, inflammation and to regulate the menstrual cycle.

Juniper

This works at all levels, but is particularly indicated for the mind, as it helps confused or conflicting thoughts and mind turmoil generally; also exhaustion caused by other people's problems. It is useful to writers and others who need to get information from the subconscious to the conscious mind. On a physical level it is a general detoxifier, cleanser and purifier. In animals, it may be used for ear canker, mange, fleas and dermatitis. It blends well with pine and sassafras.

Ylang-Ylang

This is a good base note in a blend. *Do not use it on its own.* It helps prevent hyperventilating and regulates the heart rate. It is good for shocks, over-anxiousness and frustration. It stimulates the senses and helps with sexual difficulties caused by stress. Mixed with sandalwood, it increases desire. It is an antidepressant and helps to relieve feelings of inadequacy. It reduces high blood pressure.

Benzoin

This is antiseptic and deodorant. It is also called Gum Benjamin and is an ingredient of incense. It is a good inhalant (Friar's Balsam in fact) and is also particularly useful as a healer of wounds, sores and skin irritations. It is a sedative and can be used to relieve asthma, coughs, bronchitis, laryngitis and colic. It does not evaporate quickly and makes a good fixative in a blend. It is heart-warming and has, traditionally, the Sun as its ruler.

Chamomile

This will be described under 'Herbs'. As a massage oil it is particularly good for aching muscles, especially if this is due to exertion of muscles not normally used very much.

Marjoram

This oil is primarily sedative and is warming. It helps to relieve muscle cramps and to lower high blood pressure. It is extremely valuable in a massage oil, because of its warming, comforting properties. It relieves pain and promotes the healing of bruised tissue. It is both sedative and tonic to the nervous system and probably for this reason is awarded to Mercury. However, my own feeling is that it is a herb of the Sun and Leo.

Melissa

This appears in the 'Herb' section under the name of Balm. In massage it is almost indispensable, being at once tonic and sedative, and a wonderful anti-depressant. I add it to most mixtures.

Neroli

This is orange blossom, and the oil is expensive. Luckily, only a little is needed, and it blends well with most other oils. It is a good relaxant and anti-depressant and is a valuable oil to use on those who are anxious or suffering from shock. It is undoubtedly a perfume of the Sun and of Leo. It is a good skin tonic and is absolutely safe on any type of skin.

Sandalwood

This oil is slow to evaporate and is good to mix with others for this reason. It is well known as a perfume and is much used as incense. It is soothing, tonic and sedative, but it is also an anti-depressant, which makes it eminently suitable for nervous and tense patients, especially where depression is also present. It is excellent for dry skin and for skin irritation or inflammation. It is very mild and can be used in twice the quantity of other essential oils.

For Relief of Pain

(Neuralgia, etc.) Use any three of these: Rosemary, Marjoram, Lavender, Clary Sage and Camomile.

Skin troubles

Lavender is good for an all-round skin oil and especially for Acne. With Neroli, it stimulates the growth of new cells. Camomile and/or Melissa for exzema and dermatitis, with

Lavender as a follow-up. Juniper is good for skin troubles caused by constipation, or when the body is in need of a detoxification.

Grief or Guilt

Use Juniper, Pine and Sassafras.

High Blood Pressure

Massage generally is good for this – also Ylang, Lavender and Marjoram.

For a Relaxing Massage

Add Geranium, Lavender and Marjoram to your chosen carrier oil.

For an Invigorating Massage

Use any three of Geranium, Juniper, Lavender, Marjoram, Melissa, Neroli and Sandalwood.

To Relieve mild Aches and Pains

Use two parts of Juniper to one each of Rosemary and Lavender.

To Relieve Muscle Cramps

Use any three of Juniper, Lavender, Marjoram, Neroli, Melissa, Rosemary and Sandalwood.

In general, Geranium, Lavender, and Sandalwood blend well with anything else. Geranium is particularly good for enlivening a blend and making all the ingredients come together harmoniously.

For a facial massage, Geranium, Rosemary and Juniper make a good skin tonic.

Wheatgerm oil, besides being anti-oxidant, is also rich in vitamins and will nourish the skin, as will avocado oil, but both are too heavy (and too expensive) to be used on their own. Hazelnut oil is also nourishing and penetrates the skin well without being so heavy. For general use, all the other oils mentioned are quite satisfactory, although most masseurs have their own favourites and have some with which they actually dislike to work.

In using aromatherapy for massage purposes, the chief thing to consider is that the perfume should add to the pleasure, so never use a mixture which your patient dislikes.

Stimulating or relaxing baths can be taken by adding a few drops of essence direct to a bath of water, or combining them with vegetable oil. Relaxing oils include Lavender, Marjoram, Rose, Orange Blossom, Sandalwood and Clary Sage. Tonic oils include Rosemary, Juniper, Peppermint and Basil. Lemon oil (a few drops) and juice of half a lemon, with a couple of drops of geranium oil will give you a bath which is at once refreshing and relaxing – just the thing on a hot summer day. On a winter one, you can help to prevent colds and pep up your circulation by adding Juniper, Pepper oil and Lavender oil to your bathwater.

Reflexology

The basis of this treatment is that there are reflexes in the fleshy parts of the feet which correspond to other parts of the body, including the internal organs. By working on the feet with a movement that is like a combined massage and pressure at each reflex point, it is possible to diagnose illness in another part of the body and to treat it by stimulating the organ concerned to throw off the condition. This should only be done by a trained practitioner who is aware of the amount of pressure to use and the dangers of over-stimulation. A person receiving treatment usually experiences a feeling of lightness and general well being, for which reason it is a good stimulating therapy for all who need to keep themselves fit. Discomfort will be experienced when a reflex is stimulated which corresponds to the area of the body where there is trouble, but this is only momentary and merely enables the practitioner to confirm his diagnosis. It is a good therapy for most people, except those who have foot troubles.

It is now becoming very popular and there are several good books on the subject. Unfortunately, these encourage people to think that they can learn how to be a practitioner just by reading about it. Books cannot show the amount of pressure which is safe to use and most of them do not warn the layman of possible dangers.

For instance, it is very easy to pull toes out of joint unless they are held firmly while you are working on them.

Classes are available (see 'Further Information') and potential practitioners should certainly get such training.

Potential clients should be aware of this problem and only go to reputable, fully-trained practitioners.

Pre-Natal Therapy

This involves work on the bony structure of the foot to deal with conditions which have arisen in the gestation period or in early childhood. Over a period of treatment, patients have been helped to overcome bad habits and mongoloid children have actually lost the typical mongol look. However, an adult patient needs to be willing and cooperative as personality changes are likely.

Acupuncture and Acupressure

It is not generally known that acupuncture was used by medical doctors in this country in the nineteenth and early twentieth centuries. Robert Eagle says that it was brought to Europe from China by French Jesuit priests, and he quotes from Sir William Osler's textbook *Principles and Practice of Medicine* published in 1912 in which he recommends it for lumbago.

Eagle attributes its disappearance from the medical scene as being due to the discovery of aspirin, which became the universal panacea for lumbago, rheumatic and arthritic pains. We now know the dangers and limitations of aspirin but people still prefer to go to the doctors and be given a pill rather than attempt to do something about their health themselves.

Acupuncture is now back on the scene in Europe and in America, and has achieved a great break-through since one of the American diplomats visiting China was taken ill and paid tribute to the efficacy of the acupuncture treatment which he received there.

As most people know, it consists of inserting needles into appropriate points in the body and twirling them. These points may be far removed from the seat of the trouble and this suggests an analogy with reflexology. There appear to be trigger points in the body which affect other parts of the body. Acupuncture is a proven therapy for alleviating pain. Arthritis and other back pains, migraine, asthma and other psychosomatic complaints have been successfully treated by this method.

Joseph Goodman (Dr. Ac.), Senior Lecturer at the British College of Acupuncture, explains the theory of traditional Chinese medicine, of which acupuncture is just one part, in terms that have now become familiar to us: 'Health is a measure of the free flow of energy (Ch'i) which, although indestructible in essence is capable of being obstructed.'

A skilled practitioner can diagnose the seat of the obstruction by means of four procedures which traditionally include the taking of the twelve (yes, twelve) pulses at the wrist, and then treating the patient accordingly.

Acupressure – also called *Shiat-su* – is similar except that the trigger points are activated by massage and deep pressure, and not by needles.

The danger of both methods is that the alleviation of pain may mask serious symptoms, which may not be recognised by any practitioner, who is not a skilled diagnostician. As with so many of the 'alternative medicine' practitioners, recommendation by former patients is probably the best method of choosing your own specialist. (See also Further Information.)

Chiropractic and Osteopathy

To the layman there appears to be little difference in these two techniques. In the United Kingdom they are normally used to correct spinal deficiencies by means of manipulation, though United States practitioners treat a wide variety of complaints with the same type of treatment.

Osteopaths use leverage and rotation of the limbs and also work on the soft tissue of the body. Chiropracters feel their way into the wrongly-aligned vertebrae and push them back. There is no doubt that the best of them (both osteopaths and chiropracters) are using an intuitive ability to 'sense' the source of the trouble and the right movement to correct it.

Manipulation is not taught generally within the National Health Service, although some doctors have been trying to get it accepted as part of the teaching syllabus for a very long time.

As in all the fringe medicines, most people go to chiropracters and osteopaths because they have been 'given up' by orthodox doctors. It is all the more credit to them, then, that they so often succeed where orthodox treatment has failed.

Osteopathy has now been accepted widely by the general public and increasingly by medical practitioners, who will sometimes refer their patients to an osteopath. An article in *The Times* in 1989 revealed that Geoff Capes, the shotput champion, had used the services of an osteopath for 12 years. My own family will testify that their trusted practitioner has certainly got them out of pain. Reliable practitioners can be found through the Institute for Complementary Medicine.

The Alexander Technique is a therapy for strengthening the spine. Clients are taught how to hold themselves and given appropriate exercises. They are also taught how to move. Tutors may devote hours just to teaching a client how to sit down and stand up correctly. It is not something which can be learned quickly, and, once learned, it must be consciously practised all the time.

It is therapeutic for all those who have spinal troubles, and a good preventative for those who may be subject to them. Tall people, in particular, often hold themselves badly, either in an attempt to reduce their height (if they feel self-conscious about it) or because their work causes them to stoop, and this then becomes a habit. It is particularly suggested for Leo, Sagittarius and Aquarius types.

Homoeopathy

A practitioner of homoeopathy is already a trained medical doctor. He has to pass the usual medical examinations before he is allowed to study homoeopathy. Unfortunately, the extra training, for which no grants are yet available, has become so expensive that the number of practitioners completing the training cannot keep pace with the number of patients wanting their services.

The essence of homoeopathy is that it considers the whole man; his temperament rather than his disease. For instance, the remedy prescribed for the wiry, irritable patient with a troublesome cough would be quite different from that prescribed for the more phlegmatic type with the same ailment. Symptoms are also considered in detail. Is the cough more troublesome at night or in the morning? Does it go with a high temperature? Swollen tonsils? and so on. For this reason, it is not a treatment for the layman, other than as a first aid. There are thousands of homoeopathic remedies and only a highly-skilled practitioner is likely to know just the one which is exactly right.

But homoeopathy is different from orthodox (allopathic) medicine in another fundamental way. The remedies available are prescribed in infinitesimally small quantities, and, for the most part, consist of substances that, in larger quantities, would cause the symptoms. One could describe the treatment as 'a hair of the dog that bit you'.

Dr Samuel Hahnemann was the founder of this method of treatment in the mid-eighteenth century. He evolved the 'law of similars' from the discovery that Cinchona Bark (which supplies quinine) produced symptoms similar to malaria in healthy persons. He proceeded to experiment with other medicinal substances and eventually established the principle that 'what can cause, can cure'. The preparation of the remedies begins with a genuinely natural substance (animal, vegetable or mineral). The Mother Tincture of this (indicated by Ø) is then made up into various strengths (known as potencies). Tablets are made by grinding (triturating) with sugar of milk in the proportion of one part of the substance to 99 parts of sugar of milk to give a potency of 1c (one in a hundred). This is then repeated with the already triturated 1c to give 2c or one part of the original substance in 10,000. If potencies are purchased as 1, 2, 3, etc., this is equivalent to 1c, 2c and 3c. The centesimal scale is now available in decimal scale – one part in ten – and these always carry the suffix X. 6x is a fairly common potency.

It will be appreciated that these are very small doses indeed and consequently, the danger of side effects is minimal in comparison with the massive doses of drugs used in allopathic medicine.

If you intend to keep 'first aid' remedies yourself, the 6c potency is the most useful one to have. Mother Tinctures may also be useful for *external* application *only* (tinctures are in liquid form).

Useful Mother Tinctures Ø are as follows:

Hamamelis. Ten drops to half a glass of warm water for bruises.

Calendula. As above. This tincture has many uses (see below).

Ruta. As above, for bruising of bones (and use undiluted for corns).

Rhus Tox. As above, for sprains.

In each case, lint should be wrung out in the mixture and laid over the injury, covered with flannel and bandaged.

In the case of wounds or grazes, *Calendula tincture*, made up as before, can be used for cleansing. It can also be used undiluted, as a *first* 'first aid' for burns and scalds. That is, you can pour it over the burn, while preparing a compress.

Euphrasia. Two drops in an eye-bath of water will aid in preventing irritation if dust or a foreign body gets into the eye. Here again, *Calendula tincture* makes a good substitute if Euphrasia is not available. For any eye trouble requiring bathing, one drop of Euphrasia tincture in two tablespoonsful of tepid water is useful.

The same two tinctures, *Euphrasia* or *Calendula* in the proportion of one drop to two tablespoons of cooled boiled water can be sniffed up the nose to relieve hay fever.

Ledum. Ten drops to half a teacupful of water will relieve the pain of insect stings or bites, either used as a lotion or a compress. Once again *Calendula Tincture* can also be used.

Urtica Urens made up as above should be used to relieve nettlerash and stings from plants. *Calendula tincture* can be used as a substitute.

Calendula is also useful as a mouthwash for bleeding or unhealthy gums or after dentistry. Two drops in a little water, or soda water, should be used at night.

Useful 6c potencies (in tablet form):

Aconitum. Use for feverish colds. Muscular pain caused by chills. Nervous anticipation (especially for children dreading visits to the dentist or examinations). Also for tension headaches where the patient is unable to bear the light.

Arnica. Invaluable in all cases of shock. The first remedy for accidents (including bruises and burns), also to disperse boils. This remedy is also useful in the form of ointment for bruises.

Arsen. Alb. Use for mild food poisoning (get immediate advice if it is severe). Also for diarrhoea, vomiting and runny colds.

Gelsemium. For influenza, and for nervous anticipation.

Nux. Vom. For stomach upsets and nervous indigestion, especially if caused by over-indulgence, and for constipation. Also for haemorrhoids due to too little exercise and to constipation. Useful for nervous headaches caused by anxiety.

Rhus Tox. For sprains and aching muscles caused by strain.

All the above remedies are particularly suitable to childhood ailments.

Carbo. Veg. For coughs which are worse when going from warm to cooler air. For fainting attacks with sweating or temperature drop. Also for flatulence in upper stomach with low vitality.

Hepar. Sulph. For wounds, grazes, burns or scalds if there is suppuration of matter. Also to assist boils to burst.

Urtica Urens. For burns or scalds. Can also be taken in table form for nettlerash and stings from plants, as well as used externally in tincture form.

This list would form a good nucleus for a first-aid cabinet. In addition there are some which are particularly useful to certain types of people for whom the 30 potency is recommended.

Aconitum has already been mentioned. It is indicated for people who suffer from tension with palpitations, have a dry skin and avoid the sun.

Argent. Nit. is for those who anticipate troubles and become fearful. They usually treat time as 'the enemy' and get through a great deal of work in a day.

Arsenicum is indicated for those who are tense, fastidious and fussily tidy, especially when they suffer from various fears and apprehensions for no good reason.

The *Nux Vom.* type is recognisable in the wiry, lean, dark person who feels strain or excitement in business life and is inclined to take stimulants to keep himself going. They are chilly and don't move far from the fire in winter.

Pulsatilla is indicated for the mild and good-humoured woman who weeps easily when upset or ill. I think of her as the 'fair, fat and forty' type, who cannot take fat or a rich diet without suffering for it. They dislike stuffy rooms and soon crave for fresh air.

Chamomilla is especially suitable for children who are irritable and intractable, especially when teething or when restless and not knowing what they want. (For adults, also, when they are behaving like this.)

It would be easy to classify some of these as zodiacal types, but I shall refrain from doing so. It is much better that you should treat your symptoms and personality rather then you should go for a remedy for your astrological type.

The reason for this is that our birth charts include all the zodiacal signs, whether emphasised or not, and from time to time we will undoubtedly have discomforts which do not relate to the strongest sign in our charts.

Homoeopathic remedies are useful to have in the house – particularly Arnica – but I cannot emphasise too strongly that they should be treated as a 'First Aid' only.

The Bio-Chemic Tissue Salts

There are twelve salts which are present in the body in small quantities. They are constantly being used up and then replenished from our food. Each has its own job to do and is vital to our well-being, even though we may only need a trace of it. Some zodiacal types need more of one salt because they use it up quickly or because they are unable to assimilate it from food products. These are the salts and the traditional zodiacal signs with which they are associated.

The *Aries* tissue salt is Potassium Phosphate (*Kali. Phos.*). It is a constituent of the brain cells and the nerves, and it helps to restore mental acitivity (provided the patient cooperates by resting physically and mentally). It is also indicated for the treatment of sleeplessness, nervous disorders (including those affecting the digestion) and skin troubles. It is present in a wide variety of green vegetables and potatoes, onions, apples and walnuts.

The *Taurus* salt is Sulphate of Soda (*Nat. Sulph.*), as it eliminates excess water, and is indicated for the treatment of dropsical and catarrhal conditions. It is also useful for sick headaches, liverishness, biliousness and influenza. It regulates the supply of water to the body and deficiency of this salt is indicated by heaviness at the top of the spine, chills and fever and by excessive sweating at night. Taureans need foods which keep the pores of the skin open. *Nat. Sulph.* is found in many of these, which include beetroot, cauliflower, cabbage, spinach, cucumber and onions.

The *Gemini* cell salt is Potassium Chloride (*Kali. Mur.*). This is a blood conditioner which regulates the fibrin in the blood and helps to keep it fluid. It is indicated for coughs, colds and swollen glands, and, indeed, all inflammatory diseases. Deficiency of this salt is indicated by white fibrinous discharges, showing an excess of fibrin in the blood. This condition should not be neglected otherwise the body will attempt to throw off the excess in more violent ways – by such illnesses as pleurisy and pneumonia.

This salt, also, is available in a wide range of vegetables and in many fruits including oranges, peaches, plums and pears, also in tomatoes and sweet corn.

The tissue salt for *Cancer* is Fluoride of Lime (*Calc. Fluor.*). This maintains the elasticity of tissue affecting veins, skin and all membranes. It also preserves tooth enamel (Capricorn polarity). Loss of elasticity causes cracks in the skin and lack of muscle tone, leading to prolapses, varicose veins, lower back pains, piles and poor circulation. This salt is contained chiefly in egg yolks and rye flour but it is also in most protein and vegetable foods.

Leo's tissue salt is Phosphate of Magnesia (*Mag. Phos.*). It is anti-spasmodic and is indicated for cramps, flatulence, neuralgia and all sharp, darting pains, and also for emotional exhaustion. It restores muscular tone and vigour, maintains the fluidity of the blood and revitalises the brain and nerves. Whole wheat bread, barley and rye all contain it, together with apples, lettuce, cabbage, cucumber, eggs, walnuts and figs.

The cell salt for *Virgo* is Potassium Sulphate (*Kali Sulph.*). It helps to transfer oxygen from the blood to the tissue cells, thus keeping hair, nails and skin healthy. A deficiency of it results in the clogging of the pores and impurities are not thrown off by the body. This results in catarrhal conditions. Need for this salt is shown by desire for fresh air and a continual feeling of stuffiness. Virgo people often find it difficult to assimilate this salt, which they particularly need to rebuild the nerve cells. The foods whch contain it include carrots and most salad vegetables, whole wheat, rye and oats.

Librans need Sodium Phosphate (*Nat. Phos.*), which neutralises acid and aids the digestion of fatty foods. It maintains the balance of acids and alkalis in the body. Lack of it causes all types of acidity – heartburn, poor digestion, rheumatism, etc. It revitalises the kidneys and the liver.

This tissue salt is contained in watercress, carrots, spinach, peas, celery, beetroot, apples, raisins, figs, almonds, rice and wheat.

The tissue salt for *Scorpio* is Sulphate of Lime (*Calc. Sulph.*). It is cleansing and disinfectant and promotes healing. It is found in skin, mucous membranes and tissue. Lack of it causes acne, and gumboils and other conditions where impurity of the blood is present. Suspect a deficiency of this salt if cuts are slow to heal. Its action helps to eliminate organic matter which is no longer required by the body. Constipation tends to be common in Scorpio types and this condition is an indication that *Calc. Sulph.* is not being assimilated.

Foods containing this cell salt include onions, mustard and garlic, cress, cauliflower, leeks, turnips, radishes, figs and prunes.

Silicic Oxide (*Silica*) is the cell-salt for *Sagittarians*, and, strangely, its crystal is arrow-shaped which seems appropriate for the Archer. It also has a piercing action, like an arrow, since it has the effect of puncturing boils, styes, etc., by promoting suppuration and causing the discharge of the poisonous matter. It is a cleanser and eliminator. Suspect a deficiency of this salt if you are prone to styes or boils. Brittle nails and lifeless hair are other indications that silica is not being assimilated. It is a constituent of the nerves and the bones, and helps to maintain body warmth.

The fibrous matter of fruit, vegetables and cereals all contain silica. Unfortunately, it is the skins of the fruit and vegetables and the bran which usually get discarded. They are an important source of this salt and should be used as often as possible.

The cell salt of *Capricorn* is Calcium Phosphate (*Calc. Phos.*), which builds bones and teeth. It carries albumen from the food to do this, and if it is deficient the excess albumen can cause kidney troubles, stones or skin troubles. *Calc. Phos.*, helps digestion and assimilation of food and is a good tonic. Lack of it will show in lassitude, dental troubles, chilblains and weak digestion. This latter may cause the formation of acid in the joints, which leads to rheumatism and arthritis.

Calc. Phos. is contained in spinach, cucumber, lettuce, figs, plums, strawberries, almonds, lentils and other pulses, whole wheat, barley and rye, fish and milk.

Sodium Chloride (*Nat. Mur.*), or common salt, is the tissue salt for *Aquarians*. It is a distributor and balancer of the water content of the body, and as Aquarians tend to eliminate salt from the body very quickly it needs to be constantly replaced. Either watery symptoms – streaming colds, watery eyes, wet eczema – or excessively dry conditions of the skin or mucous membranes are signs of the need for this salt. Lack of it also slows down the digestive process.

Foods containing it include spinach, cabbage, cucumber, lettuce, chestnuts and lentils, carrot, radish, apples, figs and strawberries.

The cell salt of *Pisces* is Phosphate of Iron (*Ferr. Phos.*). This is the number one biochemic remedy and first aid, as it combines with many of the other salts to aid them in their work. It oxygenates the blood and is the main ingredient in all tonics. It gives strength and elasticity to the walls of the blood vessels and arteries and prevents them hardening in later life. It is useful in the treatment of sore throats, coughs and colds and also in feverish conditions and inflammations. Applied externally, it can staunch bleeding. It combines particularly well with *Kali Mur.*, for the treatment of inflammations and with *Kali Sulph.*, for skin disorders.

It is indicated in anaemic conditions and catarrhal conditions caused by failure of the pores of the skin to throw off toxic waste.

This is one of the tissue salts which is almost totally discarded when vegetables are boiled and the water thrown away. It is present in lettuce, radishes, spinach, strawberries, lentils, onions and barley.

The tissue salts are one form of medication that can be used safely by the layman. Any amount taken which is surplus to requirements will be eliminated by the body with no harmful effects. They are easily purchased in tablet form from any Health Food store and many chemists, especially homoeopathic ones.

The reason why the tissue salts can be assimilated by the body in the form of prepared tablets, even where they are not assimilated from food, is explained by the preparation of the tablets. These are triturated to refine the salts and to make them immediately accessible. The tablets (which are tasteless) dissolve on the tongue and the salts are absorbed directly into the bloodstream. They have no side effects, as they are not drugs, and they will not affect, or be affected by, any other medicines.

As with all forms of treatment, symptoms are likely to persist and even increase for a day or two – this is merely a sign that the treatment is working – and this should be regarded as a good sign. It is comparable to a 'healing crisis' which may occur just before a fever breaks. However, any symptoms which persist and become chronic should never be treated without professional help.

Combinations of the tissue salts for specific ailments are now available at health shops and at least one of the well-known High Street chemists.

Herbs

Many herbs are of value for dietary purposes and as aids to healing.

Of the hundreds available I have chosen to describe less than fifty, because these are easily obtainable and are all safe for the layman to use. Others should only be used as advised by a herbalist, as many are toxic if taken in sufficient quantity.

In many cases it is obvious that the herb described helps a wide variety of symptoms and I have not attempted to give each one an astrological 'ruler'. Culpeper's *Complete Herbal* is the most noted for linking herbs to astrology, but as David Conway remarks in *The Magic of Herbs*, he was often guilty of making them fit, and I have not hesitated to disagree with him. No matter which astrological sign or planet is allocated to a herb, if it is of benefit for those 'ruled' by other signs, you will find it recommended for them under the heading of their zodiacal sign.

Where I have not specified the method of preparation, 1 oz (25 g) of the chopped herb to 1 pint (550 ml) of boiling water is the usual infusion.

Alfalfa (Medicago sativa)

This is one of the valuable herbs which has become widely available for purchase in the form of seeds (for sprouting – see 'Diet'). It is strengthening and weight adding. The seeds used whole or powdered with cider vinegar and honey have proved a valuable treatment for arthritis.

Angelica (Angelica officinalis)

Stimulates the digestive juices and the appetite. The root and the seeds are both of use for all digestive problems, especially heartburn, and all stomach complaints. Useful for colic in children and for sore tonsils. According to Culpeper, it is a herb of the Sun and Leo, which is probably correct as it has tonic properties.

Arrowroot (Maranta arundinacer)

This is easy to buy as a powder and is a well-known remedy for calming the stomach and stopping vomiting. It can be used with milk and a sweetening agent to make a palatable blanc-mange to halt excessive purging.

Balm (Melissa officinalis)

An easily-grown herb which can be taken as a tea (an infusion of 1 oz (25 g) chopped leaves to 1 pint (550 ml) boiling water). As its name implies, it is soothing for the stomach and digestive tract and cooling for feverish complaints. It is good for nervous troubles, infertility, and irregular menses, for which reason it is reputed to be a herb of Cancer, though Culpeper also assigns it to Jupiter. The leaves may be eaten raw. A valuable herb which fully lives up to its name.

Basil (Ocimum basilicum)

This is another easily-grown aromatic herb. It helps the digestion and heals wounds. It is excellent for nervous disorders, and for morning sickness and travel sickness. It is unusual in being both a stimulant and a nervine, as nervines are usually sedative. It can be freely added to soups and salads or used as a tea (1 teaspoonful of chopped leaves to a potful of water). Culpeper attributes it to Mars and Scorpio, probably for its stimulant properties and for the healing of wounds.

Bay (Laurus nobilis)

This is commonly grown as a tree and the dried leaves are easily purchased for culinary use. It stimulates the appetite and helps to dissolve obstructions in the liver and spleen. The oil is valuable for skin troubles, including bruising, as it dissolves the congealed blood. It is difficult to see why Culpeper attributes this herb to the Sun and Leo. My own preference is for Jupiter and Sagittarius.

Bergamot (Monarda didyma)

This is a relaxant and helps to induce sleep. It gives Earl Grey tea its distinctive flavour, in which form it is widely available. It can be added to potpourri in the form of oil, to refresh it, and this can be left in bedrooms to help relaxation. The oil should not be used on the skin, where it can cause a rash if exposed to the sun. In my opinion, this is a herb of Pisces.

Bilberry (Vaccinium myrtillus)

The ripe fruits are valuable for all cases of water retention, especially dropsical conditions, and gravel. 1 oz (25 g) of berries to 1 pint (550 ml) of boiling water makes a refreshing drink. A wine-glassful of this is cooling, astringent and diuretic. It is probably a herb of Jupiter.

Blackberry (Rubus fructicosus)

All parts of this shrub can be used. The fruits are good for anaemia. The root will cure diarrhoea in children. The leaves should be infused as for blackcurrant and used as an aperient and tonic. It can be applied externally for psoriasis. Taken as a tea, it is an excellent blood purifier.

Blackcurrant (Ribes nigrum)

The leaves of this shrub are detergent and cooling. Use 1 oz (25 g) of chopped leaves, or the ripe fruit, to 1 pint (550 ml) boiling water for a well-known cure for throat infections, hoarseness and catarrh. It is also valuable for whooping cough. It breaks fevers and inflammation. Being rich in vitamin C it is tonic and nutritive. It is probably a herb of Taurus, as it used for the prevention and treatment of goitre.

Borage (Borage officinalis)

This is a common garden herb, which deserves to be more widely grown. It contains potassium and calcium and is a good blood purifier and nerve tonic. It smells like cucumber and has the same cooling effect. Above all, it is a stimulant and anti-depressant. It activates the adrenal glands, heart, kidneys and digestive system. A wineglassful of the tea – 1 oz (25 g) leaves to 1 pint (550 ml) boiling water – will help to abate fever. It is a cure for jaundice and increases the milk flow of the nursing mother. It can be used as a poultice for inflammation and swellings. Culpeper ascribes it to Jupiter and Leo, but I favour Mars and Aries as its rulers for it is noted for imparting courage.

Camphor (Cinnamomum camphora)

This is widely available as oil. It can be applied externally for bruises, sprains and inflammation and taken for fever and hysterical complaints. Cold chills, rheumatic and neuralgic pains may all be eased by it. I suggest that it is a herb of Saturn and Capricorn.

Caraway (Carum carvi)

One of our most useful herbs which should be grown by everyone with a garden. Root, leaf and seed all have their uses. The roots should be used as a vegetable and the leaves in salad. The seeds can be made into a herbal tea which will relieve colds, stimulate digestion and lactation and soothe fretful children. As a poultice, it will draw boils and strengthen sprained limbs. Culpeper awards it to Mercury, perhaps because of its versatility.

Cayenne (Capsicum frutescens)

This is easy to purchase as a powder. It is a stimulant and tonic, a body purifier and disinfectant. It wards off infections and colds and checks nosebleeding. It can, however, cause reddening of the skin, and it has been attributed to Aries – correctly, I believe.

Chamomile (Anthemis nobilis)

This is widely available as a tea – 1 oz (25 g) to 1 pint (550 ml) of boiling water. It is definitely an acquired taste and some people find it more palatable with added honey. It helps digestive, nervous and hysterical complaints. It also helps to dissolve tumours and ulcers. It can be used externally for neuralgia, toothache and earache and makes a good mouthwash after dental treatment. It relieves tiredness and revives the system, and it is probably for this reason that Culpeper attributes it to the Sun.

Chicory (*Chichorium intybus*)

The root is used in coffee mixtures to counteract the stimulating effect of the coffee. 1 oz (25 g) root to 1 pint (550 ml) boiling water can be made into a tea and taken freely as a tonic. It is also diuretic and laxative. It is good for liver conditions, gout and rheumatism. It breaks down gall stones and eliminates excess mucus. I think it is probably a herb of Jupiter.

Cloves (*Symphytum officinale*)

This is grown in the East but the clove seeds and clove oil are widely available. It is soothing and antiseptic, being a well-known remedy for toothache. As a tea, or cordial, it is warming, strengthening and stimulating. It relieves nausea, clears stomach gases and purifies the abdomen. For the latter, a few drops of clove oil in a little water is the quickest road to relief.

Comfrey (*Symphytum*)

This plant is very easy to grow – in fact it will soon take over the garden if left. It is also easy to find growing wild. The leaves can be eaten in salad, or dried and made into a tea. It was known from ancient times as the all-healer. Its old country name of Knitbone gives the clue to its chief virtues. It is good for rheumatism and all bone troubles (including breaks and sprains), and makes a good cold compress for eye injuries. It is used externally for the skin, bruises and insect bites, and helps to prevent colds. Recent research has isolated a substance in it which may cause cancer, but its users swear by it, and I take the view of the Herbal Society that many things we eat have trace elements of harmful substances which are not present in sufficient quantity to do us harm. (In this case, *massive* doses had been given to laboratory animals.) I agree with Culpeper that this is a herb of Saturn and Capricorn.

Dandelion (Taraxacum officinale)

Both root and leaves can be used. It cleanses the blood stream and is tonic and diuretic. It is a valuable herb, being rich in vitamins A, B, and C. The root can be roasted and ground to make a coffee-like drink and the leaves can be eaten in salads. It is good for liver and kidney disorders and it helps to prevent arthritis by dispersing acidic deposits from the joints. Culpeper says it is a herb of Jupiter, but it is so good for so many conditions that I think it is a herb of the Sun and Leo (as the 'sunny' appearance of the flower would indicate).

Dill (Anethum graveolens)

This is well known as an ingredient in gripe water which is used to soothe babies. It helps to stop vomiting and hiccups and checks halitosis. It will cleanse the digestive tract and inhibit ulcers and, for this reason, is judged to be a herb of Mercury and Virgo.

Elderberry (Sambus nigra)

This is another valuable herb as flowers, berries and leaves are all used. Elderflower tea is sleep-inducing and a mild astringent for the skin. It is a splendid spring tonic and blood purifier and helps rheumatic and catarrhal conditions. The berries reduce fever, promote perspiration and soothe burns and scalds. The leaves can also be used as a tea and help in all dropsical conditions, so this is likely to be a herb of Venus.

Eyebright (Euphrasia officinalis)

This is a common herb, although Euphrasia tincture may also be easily purchased. The leaves can be dried and boiled. This makes an effective lotion for all eye troubles. As a tea it is good for gastric and gall bladder troubles. Culpeper says it improves the memory and gives its rulership to Leo and the Sun. I am inclined to give it to Aries as the ruler of the eyes.

Fennel (Foeniculum vulgare)

The seeds of this herb are easy to purchase. Its oil is a good disinfectant. A teaspoonful of seed boiled in 1/2 pint (275 ml) of milk and allowed to boil for ten minutes and then strained makes a tea which will relieve flatulence and colic in babies. It is a restorative following strokes. This tea is also good for nursing mothers. A compress of the seeds relieves inflammation of the eyes. A valuable herb for Virgo types, to which sign I would give rulership.

Fenugreek (Trigonella foenum graecum)

Like alfalfa, this has become widely available as seed for sprouting. The ground seeds can be used as a poultice for abscesses and boils. A teaspoonful of ground seed to 1/2 pint (275 ml) of boiling water is good for sore throats, and for inflammation of the stomach and intestines. It is a strong antiseptic. The sprouted seeds are nutritious used as a salad.

Feverfew (Tanacetum parthenium, sometimes listed as Chrysanthemum parthenium)

A breakthrough in recent years has been the growing recognition of the uses for this herb. Although there are references to it in ancient Greece, it is only recently that medical enquiries have been made to determine its action in the body.

It seems to be an anti-inflammatory agent, counteracting substances which cause the pains of migraine and arthritis. It may also be helpful for other stress-related problems such as psoriasis, PMT and muscular cramp.

This herb is easy to grow, but make sure that you get the correct variety. Some of the feverfew on sale may not be the right plant, so it is safer to grow and dry your own. It is easy to use if finely ground and put into a salt cellar. You can then shake about half a small mustard spoonsful over savoury food.

It can be bought in this form from the Dooley Feverfew Company, Dooley House, Carters Lane, Wickham Bishops, Witham, Essex CM8 3LF (tel. 0631–891–642). The company sends a great deal of valuable information with its product, which is organically grown under controlled conditions.

Garlic (Allium sativum)

This is a good general tonic, building resistance to disease and infection. It stimulates the digestion and relieves rheumatism. It is also excellent for the chest and lungs. Culpeper gives its rulership to Mars, which is likely to be correct for its qualities as a stimulant.

Ginger (Zinigiber officianale)

Tea made from the root makes a good gargle. As a tea or a syrup it is a good cough remedy.

Ginseng (Panax quinquefolium or P. Schin-seng)

The powdered root of this herb is easily purchased. Many claims have been made for it and, no doubt, some are wildly exaggerated, but it is certainly a good stimulant and tonic for the whole nervous system. It helps conditions of nervous or mental exhaustion. It improves the appetite and digestion and relieves stomach ailments. It has a reputation as an aphrodisiac and it is likely that it stimulates the pituitary and adrenal glands. Probably a herb of Mars and Scorpio.

Hops (Humulus lupulus)

It is possible to purchase hop pillows to cure insomnia. Hops taken as tea will have the same effect and will aid the digestion. The herb has been attributed by Culpeper to Mars and by other writers to Aries specifically.

Horseradish (*Armoracia rusticana*)

Grated horseradish root can be used as a poultice as it is antiseptic and healing. A teaspoonful taken neat, or spread on bread and butter, will relieve bronchial catarrh and reduce internal growths and tumours. It stimulates the glandular system to throw off poisons and helps kidney disorders. Despite its hot taste, which has led some writers to attribute it to Scorpio, I think it is a herb of Libra.

Hyssop (*Hyssopus officinalis*)

This is an easily-grown herb with a delightful aroma. It is a great cleanser and promotes healing. The crushed leaves can be applied to wounds to prevent infection. It relieves catarrh, regulates blood-pressure, and reduces the secretion of mucus. It is a herb of Jupiter, helping all liver conditions, especially jaundice. *Warning: large doses can cause vomiting.* Used externally, it will relieve bruising and inflammation.

Kelp (*Macorcystis pyrifera*)

The value of kelp has long been recognised as a source of natural iodine and is easy to purchase in the form of tablets. It helps to prevent goitre, and is especially rich in iron. This makes it particularly beneficial to Pisceans, to which sign I would give rulership.

Lavender (*Lavandula officinalis or L. Vera, etc.*)

This herb is well known for its refreshing perfume. It soothes nerves and helps headaches and migraine, faintness or dizziness. It revives and relieves tiredness. As a gargle it is antiseptic and cures halitosis. Culpeper says it is a herb of Mercury. I would go further and award it to Gemini.

Lovage (Levisticum officinalis)

This is an easily-grown herb, which is an excellent skin cleanser. It is carminative, diuretic and stimulant and will be found useful for fevers, stomach disorders and dysmenorrhea. According to Culpeper it belongs to the Sun and Taurus.

Mint (Mentha viridis)

This is well known and is easily made into a tea. It helps the digestion and revives the appetite. It is also said to cure impotence.

Mustard (Sinapis nigra)

Plasters made from mustard are a well-known remedy for rheumatic and back pains. Mustard baths help to prevent chills after exposure to the elements. The seeds can be eaten to help weak stomachs and prevent indigestion. They contain sulphur and the undiluted oil is *dangerous* to the skin.

Nettle (Urtica dioica)

Another valuable herb, which deserves a better fate than to be rooted out as a weed. The flowers, leaves and seed are all usable. It is an excellent blood purifier and spring tonic. The leaves can be boiled and eaten as a vegetable and will improve poor circulation and help rheumatic conditions. 1 oz (25 g) of the chopped herb or seed to 1 pint (550 ml) of boiling water makes a tea which can be used for coughs. It stimulates the digestion and promotes lactation. It is astringent, diuretic, nutritive and tonic. Culpeper assigns it to Mars, probably because of its stimulative effect.

Olive (Olea europaea)

Olive oil is easy to purchase and is a well-known cure for burns and bruises. It is also useful as a gentle laxative, and for diseases of the bowels. It helps to soothe teething infants.

Parsley (Carum petroselinum)

This is rich in vitamins A, B and C and contains many minerals. Some can be eaten, with advantage, every day. It is a tonic for the urinary system, bladder and kidneys. It is a nervine and blood purifier. It stimulates the digestion and tones up the digestive system. I have seen it attributed to Mars, Gemini and Mercury. I disagree with all the experts and think that it is a herb of Libra.

Pennyroyal (Mentha pulegium)

This is a type of mint and is an easily-grown herb. It is warming and soothing. As a weak tea it is good for feverish or teething infants.

Peppermint (Mentha piperata)

This can be easily purchased as distilled oil. It allays flatulence and nausea, helps digestion generally and revives the appetite. A few drops added to water will improve skin disorders.

Rosemary (Rosmarinus officinalis)

This easily-grown aromatic herb is a heart and liver tonic, which reduces high blood pressure. 1 oz (25 g) to 1 pint (550 ml) boiling water makes a tea which is good for neuralgia and as a nerve sedative. It is digestive and stimulates the circulation. It is said to improve the memory. Used as a hair tonic it prevents baldness. I concur with Culpeper who says this is a herb of the Sun.

Sage (Salvia officinalis)

Applied directly to wounds, sage leaves will staunch bleeding. A teaspoonful of dried sage to $^1/_2$ pint (275 ml) of water –

steeped, but not boiled – will heal quinsy and ulcerated throats (a teacupful should be taken night and morning). It also makes a good gargle for a sore throat. The tea will control dizziness and emotional excitement. It is a nervine and helps the liver, bile and digestive system. Culpeper says this is a herb of Taurus. *Warning: Sage should not be eaten in large quantities by pregnant women.*

Sunflower (Helianthus annuus)

The seeds are easily purchased and are very palatable. They are a valuable source of vitamin B. 2 oz (50 g) of seeds to 1 quart of boiled water, allowed to reduce to 3/4 pint (425 ml) makes a good tea for bronchitis, laryngitis, coughs and colds and helps to prevent infection. This herb is diuretic and expectorant. A herb of Taurus.

Thyme (Thymus serpyllum or T. Vulgaris)

A well-known aromatic herb, easily grown. It is cleansing and antiseptic. It is good for feverish conditions and the digestion. A poultice of the leaves reduces inflammation. It is a good liver tonic and cures headaches and giddiness resulting from kidney troubles. There is wide agreement that it is a herb of Venus and Libra. *Warning: This herb assimilates lead. Do not gather it from road sides. It is safest to grow it yourself.*

Witch Hazel (Hamamelis)

This is easy to purchase and is a good general healer. It is astringent and antiseptic and checks haemorrhages, piles and pyorrhea. It should be applied externally in the form of ointment or liquid. The liquid can be used to massage the gums.

Yerba Mate (Ilex paraguensis)

This is now easily purchased as a green tea. It is a stimulant, and has been found useful to counteract rheumatism and gout.

The Bach Flower Remedies

Like the homoeopathic remedies, the Bach flower remedies are aimed at treating the person, rather than the disease, and, in particular, the mental state of the person.

The flowers are an extension of the herbal medicines already familiar to most of us. They were discovered in the 1930s by Dr Edward Bach, MB, BS, LRCP, MRCS, DPH. He abandoned his practice to seek a method of curing the sick that could have no ill-effects. He believed that to treat the patient was to treat the disease and that 'the mind, being the most delicate part of the body, shows the onset of disease more definitely than the body', and so he chose the state of mind as the guide to which remedy was necessary. In view of what we now know about psychosomatic illness his ideas must commend themselves to us.

Dr Arthur Bailey prefers the flower remedies to the tissue salts (though he uses both) as giving the quickest relief. These are a safe form of treatment for the layman. They are stocked by homoeopathic chemists and by some health-food stores. The extracts are in liquid form and, as only a very small dose is required, you can make up your own bottle of the remedy by adding two drops of the purchased remedy to a small bottle of water. If you need to keep it for some time, add a little brandy to the water as a preservative.

A dose consists of a few drops from your made-up bottle, which can again be diluted with a little water or milk (or taken neat in an emergency). Doses can be safely given at intervals of anything from a few minutes to two or three hours.

The same bottle can be used to provide a lotion – a few drops in a bowl of water – to relieve pain, inflammation or stiffness. Since it is easy to prepare the flower remedies for your own use, here is the most usual method.

If possible, obtain some pure spring water and pick your blooms in the early morning when they are at their freshest. You also need to choose a bright, sunny day.

Put the water into a glass bowl (not thick glass) and float the blossoms on top of the water so that they completely cover the surface. Stand the bowl in bright sunshine for three or four hours, or until the blooms begin to fade. Your water is now charged with the essence of the flowers and is ready for use as a stock bottle (that is, a bottle from which you take two drops and then dilute it). Pour the liquid into a bottle which it will half fill and then top up with brandy.

If it is not possible to obtain pure spring water, use the purest water you can get.

This is a suitable method of preparation for Agrimony, Rock Rose, Mimulus, Cerato, Chicory, Clematis, Centaury, Gentian, Impatiens, Scleranthus, Vervain and Water Violet.

These were the original twelve remedies, although the Dr Edward Bach Centre now supplies thirty-eight, and Dr Arthur Bailey has devised his own by dowsing over plants to see whether they are suitable for medical treatments.

There is another method of preparation which is suitable when you wish to use other parts of the plant, such as small pieces of stems or fresh leaves. In these cases, the specimens should be boiled for 30 minutes in fresh water (as pure as possible). This should then be allowed to cool, strained and bottled as before, allowing room to add the brandy when the essence is cold. This method is used to prepare Aspen, Beech, Crab Apple, Elm, Gorse, Heather, Holly, Hornbeam, Oak, Olive, Pine, etc.

The Bach Centre places the remedies under seven headings according to the mood of the patient – fearful, uncertain, lacks interest in present situation, lonely, over-sensitive to other influences, despondent or despairing and over-caring for others. Other books are available which give more precise descriptions of the various moods.

I will describe the moods which indicate the original twelve flower remedies.

Agrimony. This is the remedy for the cheerful type of people who are easily distressed by quarrels. They tend to hide their troubles from others, but may take stimulants as a means of coping with them. They dislike being alone and enjoy excitement. They tend to be nervous and anxious and have a dread of physical illness. However, they have no fear of death and can become suicidal under extreme anxiety. They are over-influenced by other people, because they want to avoid controversy and also because they are basically kind.

Centaury is the flower for those who want to do too much for other people. They are usually quiet and gentle and have a strong sense of service, which may cause them to over-drive themselves. They often do far more than their share of the work. They should take Centaury when they feel dominated by others (especially if they have been misguided by other people) and when feeling over-sensitive or exhausted. These people can deny themselves and make martyrs of themselves. They are often weak-willed and can permit others to sap their vitality.

Cerato is indicated for people who have so little confidence in themselves that they will not make their own decisions and perpetually seek other people's advice. They can be changeable and lack concentration. They rarely hold strong convictions about anything, but are always seeking for information and asking questions. They are nervously talkative and tend to drain other people of energy.

Chicory belongs to those who are over protective of others. They like their loved ones always near to them. They tend continually to interfere in other people's affairs 'for their own good' and are always finding something to put right. They dislike being alone and want to 'possess' others. They tend to enjoy arguments and to be 'bossy', and are capable, but fussy. They have a great fear of losing friends despite the fact that they are always finding fault with them. They are likely to suffer from feelings of mental congestion and tend to become hypochondriac to win sympathy and to keep their power over others. They are easily irritated and 'nervy' and are victims of self-pity. They have strong wills and their concern for others masks the fact that they are basically self-centred and will sap other people's vitality with their fussy interfering. They are victims of worrying and weep easily.

Clematis. This is for those who have not much interest in their life. They tend to be withdrawn, quiet and dreamy, and to live in the future in the hope that it may be better, without apparently considering trying to change the present. These are the people who give up easily if they become ill. They may appear absent-minded or absorbed in thought but lack concentration. They appear to have no ambitions and can best be described as apathetic. They easily become exhausted, due to lack of vitality. They are impractically idealistic and imaginative. They can draw illness to them as a means of escape from experiences, and this may take the form of religious obsessions and even insanity. These people are extremely sensitive to noise. Normally, they are uncomplaining (simply because they are not interested) even though they are often unhappy. What little vitality they have is easily sapped by other people. They have no fear of death and sometimes seem to welcome it.

Gentian is indicated for those people who give up easily. Even when their affairs are going well, a small hitch disheartens them. This is the type who makes mountains out of molehills. They are easily depressed and discouraged. They are easily influenced by any delay or hindrance and full of self doubts and loss of faith. These people can fall into melancholic states for no obvious reason.

Impatiens. The name describes the people for whom this is indicated. They are quick in thought and in action and will brook no delay to their plans. They cannot bear to be ill and will often force the pace of their convalescence. They are impatient with slower people and, for this reason, often choose to work alone. The late Charles Carter, the well-known astrologer, confessed that this was his remedy. Impatiens subjects are usually capable and tend to over-exert themselves. They have plenty of self-assurance and self-reliance with high ideals, but they are intolerant of restraint and tend to criticise and hurry other people. They can make hard taskmasters, being quite unaware that other people do not have their abundant energy. Their illnesses spring from restlessness and irritability, strain and tension, all caused by the inability to relax.

Mimulus is indicated for those who are fearful of life and who tend to keep their fears to themselves. They dread the possibility of illness, accidents, loneliness, etc. – all the natural hazards of life. They are nervous and hesitant and they do not like to be alone, yet at the same time they do not like a lot of company. They are quite capable of being ill to escape from certain fears. They are usually shy and quiet people, and they put off taking action for as long as possible. They lack self-confidence and react badly to noise or arguments, they are easily frightened by any adversity, and, although they have a fear of death, they can become suicidal under tension. Other people can drain them of energy.

Rock Rose. This is the remedy to grab in any emergency – an accident or sudden illness, or in a case of shock. It has been called 'The Rescue Remedy', but it is now possible to purchase a remedy called 'Rescue' which combines Rock Rose with four other flower extracts and which, in the words of the suppliers, 'meets all emergency states – terror, shock, mental tension and loss of emotional control', and I recommend that it should be kept readily available by everyone.

Rock Rose is indicated for those who are apprehensive, or despairing, also following nightmares or bad dreams, or in any other cases of extreme fear, hopelessness or panic. It is number one in the list of flower remedies, and rightly so, for it is one we all need on occasions. We should be aware that more people die of shock than any other symptoms following an accident and this (together with 'Rescue' remedy) is the quickest way I know to counteract shock. In an emergency, tip up the bottle and swallow it neat – don`t waste precious time measuring out doses.

Scleranthus. This is for those quiet people who suffer agonies of indecision from seeing both sides of the question.

This problem is not discussed with other people. It is indicated for moodiness and changeability, also for lack of concentration through indecision. The problem gives rise to lack of self-confidence and instability and can lead to nervous breakdowns. The patient's reactions may be slow and he tends to delay taking action. The unstable may become violent or tearful.

Vervain. This is the remedy for the Fixed signs of the zodiac (Taurus, Leo, Scorpio and Aquarius), and for all who rarely change their opinions, as they are not open to other people's ideas. They, also, tend to over care for other people, and, being strong-willed try to dominate them and convert them to their own way of thinking even though they also worry over them. They have plenty of courage and do not give in to illness, often pushing themselves when they should rest. They enjoy arguments and like to direct other people's affairs. They frequently suffer from exhaustion, due to the fact that they over-concentrate and put too much effort and strain into their activities. They seek for power and can be hard task-masters to those under them. They have high ideals, however, and will make themselves martyrs to a cause about which they feel passionately. All efforts are taken to excess and this leads to 'nerviness' and eventually to nervous breakdowns. They possess plenty of self-confidence and tend to be quick in action despite the rigidity of their minds and attitudes. They suffer from tension and strain and can become violent. Their vitality drains energy from others.

Water Violet is for the 'loner'. These people are usually very quiet and gentle, although they are competent and self-reliant. Often they are clever people who appear to others to be aloof. They do not worry about other people's opinions and are usually peaceful and calm within. They have a definite need to be alone and will avoid arguments. Because of their self-reliance they are valuable people to have around in an emergency.

It is obvious that the states described above tend to be extreme, and although it is tempting to ascribe them to zodiacal signs (since some obviously fit exactly) I have refrained from doing so because the complications of the full birth chart will reveal that most people fall into two or more categories. I have, however, included some suggestions for the use of the Bach remedies under the description of each zodiacal sign, including some which have not been described here, where appropriate.

These are very safe remedies and you can use them without fear of any side effects, but *do not* use them to mask symptoms which persist and which need skilled attention. Most health stores stock them.

Treating the Whole Person

It has long been clear to most practitioners of alternative therapies that treating the body is not enough. We are, in the words of the Psalmist, 'fearfully and wonderfully made' physically, but we are also beings of mind and spirit. Full health is only enjoyed when we are whole in every part of our being.

The appreciation of this fact has led to the founding of several charities which offer complete treatment of the whole person. All of these now involve orthodox medical practitioners who have become convinced that holistic treatment is the way forward.

Counselling is recognised as an essential part of any treatment, and rightly so, since it is often a problem at home or at work which has been a barrier to a patient's full recovery (or even the original cause of illness). These problems may not be solved, or even be capable of a solution, but we can learn how to deal with them so that they no longer disrupt our lives or threaten our physical health.

To anyone who has not experienced counselling, this statement will seem like arrant nonsense. 'How can anyone else help me with an insoluble problem?' is likely to be the reaction of a victim caught in a 'no win' situation. While this is understandable, the fact remains that many people have been shown how to change *their* reactions and attitudes so that problems become outgrown – in effect, one rises above them, and they cease to affect the quality of life.

In my book *Self-Development with Astrology* I have given several examples of cases which looked so hopeless to the victim, but in which the situation was radically changed as a result of counselling.

The Blackthorn Trust writes about self-healing and patient power in its literature. It offers counselling, medicaments from natural sources, eurythmy and artistic therapies. This Trust has attracted NHS funding and among its satisfied customers are patients with Multiple Sclerosis and Parkinsons disease.

We believe that possibly as many as 90 per cent of cancer patients have a background of tension, frustration or resentment – often bottled-up for years. Counselling, which encourages them to release these feelings in controlled conditions, has done wonders for many known to us personally.

One of my husband's patients was urged by him to have a lump in her stomach investigated – just in time, as it happened. She had a cancerous growth removed immediately and then received radiation therapy, as a result of which she looked very frail and bowed. We persuaded her to go to the Bristol Cancer Help Centre. After a week there, followed by a short holiday, she came back looking like a different person. Two years on, she is still very fit and enjoying life. Her problems have not disappeared but she has learnt not to let them upset her, knowing that her health is more important, and making sure that she gets time for herself. The Centre offers dietary advice, meditation, counselling and artistic therapies, etc.

The Marylebone Health Centre is in the crypt of St Marylebone Parish Church. There you will find practitioners of homoeopathy, osteopathy, traditional Chinese medicine, massage, counselling and herbal remedies. In addition, there are a wide range of activities, some involving the whole family. Practical help is also given by putting people in touch with each other for baby-sitting, help with transport, and so on.

The principal partner in this enterprise is Dr Patrick C. Pietroni, FRCGP, MRCP, DCH, who is a general practitioner at St Mary's Hospital Medical School. His book, *The Greening of Medicine* relates the story of the centre and of its counterpart in Wales. I recommend this book for its wide-ranging subject matter on all aspects of the new thinking about health.

The Institute for Complementary Medicine recognises therapists who have been trained by approved bodies and will supply information about registered practitioners. It also has Public Information Points (PIPs) for many areas. Your local library may have the telephone number for one in your region.

Information may often be available in local health stores and in the magazines which they sell. Many health stores sell the remedies mentioned here and also a wide range of books about the various treatments.

THE REGIME FOR HEALTH

Diet

A few years ago a report appeared in the newspapers of an address that Professor John Yudkin had just given to an all-party meeting in the House of Commons. They quoted him as saying, 'we now have an enormous range of foods that bring little in the way of nutrients. These not only push more nutritious foods out of the diet, they also encourage overeating and obesity'. He talked about the advance of technology in Western countries producing 'a state of malnutrition of affluence'.

At the same time, a well-known women's magazine was warning, 'It is believed that eating over-refined foods can cause cancer of the bowel'.

Why have we let our national diet get into this state? Sad to say, it is partly because it is more profitable for flour millers to sell the bran part of the wheat for cattle food and to sell the wheat germ separately. The 'flour' which is left is so lacking in nutrition that chemical additives are needed *by law* in order to bring it up to even the low standard required. In addition, there is usually a chemical preservative in it to improve the 'shelf life' (that is, the length of time during which it appears to remain 'fresh'). The result is that our farm animals are better fed than we are while we consume a large quantity of 'non-foods' in the course of a day.

The other reason is that we have got used to convenience foods and demand that everything should come to us pre-packed or tinned and with good keeping quality. The result is that various types of preservatives are used (including sodium nitrate, which has recently come under suspicion as a possible cause of cancer) and that white sugar, in particular, is 'refined' to the stage where it contains *nothing but carbohydrates*. It does not offer you a single vitamin or mineral – in other words, it is practically a non-food.

There used to be an old country saying that 'you have to eat a peck of dirt before you die', but in those days the 'dirt' had not been sprayed with chemical fertilizers and what was not washed off the vegetables probably would not have done you much harm. It is a different story today, and all shop bought fruit and vegetables need to be well washed in the hope that we are thereby getting rid of as much as possible of the offending chemicals.

Today we are bombarded with diet advice from many sources – some of which is contradicted a few months later. I will say more on that subject, but first I will give you the history of some of our common foods, so that you may judge for yourself.

Types of Flour

Wheats can be 'strong' or 'weak' according to the hardness of the grain and the quality of the gluten, but all have the same structure – six layers of outer skin, the germ and the endosperm. The first five layers are the bran which is rich in minerals, the sixth layer contains protein and fat as well as minerals, the germ contains a high percentage of wheat oil, phosphates, active enzymes and sugar, and the endosperm contains *only starch*. It is this latter from which white (or refined) flour is made. No wonder that bread is called 'the staff of life', but see how little of the 'life-giving' part is used for our white bread. The bran and fibre is sold for animal food (literally, casting the pearl before the swine), while the wheat germ is extracted to be sold separately to supplement diets or to be added to speciality breads. This leaves just the endosperm (the starch) for ordinary white bread, and as I have already said, it is so deficient in minerals and vitamins that synthetic ones have to be added by law.

Whole wheat flours which are stone ground retain all the goodness of the wheat. 100 per cent wholemeal is just what it says – all the wheat. 81 per cent has had 19 per cent of the bran sieved out, but still contains all the wheat germ, some bran and all the available oil. Neither of these require any additives by law. Granary bread is made from malted wholewheat with some whole grains mixed in.

Bread and pasta made with these flours are delicious, nutty in texture and very satisfying. You really will not need to eat so much of them as you do of the 'cotton wool' products of white flour because your body will get so much more nourishment from them. This is one of the reasons why, although the raw materials cost more, it can be cheaper to make whole foods your foods.

The Story of Sugar

Both cane and beet sugar are heated until they form crystals. When the plants are crushed, sweet juice flows from them – a juice which is equally as nutritious as any fruit juice, but the crystalising process (repeated three or four times) eventually 'washes out' all the nutrients and colour. 'Raw' sugar is the dark brown type which remains after the first heating and which still contains valuable iron. The lighter the sugar, the less real food it contains.

The by-product (the first juice) is known to us as molasses, and this is rich in essential minerals and also contains some vitamins and protein. It contains only 59 calories per ounce, instead of the 112 calories in an ounce of sugar (even brown sugar contains this colossal number of calories). As molasses is rich in iron, which tends to be deficient in the diet of Western countries, it is sensible to use it instead of sugar where ever possible. It is sweeter than white sugar and it contains glucose and fructose (or fruit sugar) which are less likely to cause tooth decay than sucrose (white sugar). It is absorbed more slowly into the blood and will supply energy for a longer period.

Honey – The Complete Food

We are all familiar with honey which, in its pure form (straight from the hive) is a natural energy-giving food containing nearly all the vitamins and minerals needed to sustain life. It acts quickly to restore and then maintain the level of blood sugar. It is an internal cleanser and is roughly twice as sweet as sugar and contains about eighty calories per ounce. It can be safely and beneficially given to invalids and I thoroughly recommend it for use in place of sugar where ever possible.

Unfortunately, if honey is stored or imported in bulk, it is necessary to heat it so that it will flow for bottling and also if it is sold as 'clear' honey. If you can get locally-produced honey (or some that has not been heat treated) you can be sure that it is of high quality.

Honey is known as a healer and was applied to external wounds as recently as the Second World War, but it is also a great help in preventing and relieving arthritis and migraine when combined with cider vinegar. These are the ingredients for a pleasant and refreshing drink. Take two teaspoons of honey and two teaspoons of cider vinegar, adding hot or cold water to taste. I use about half a glass of water, but if this is too sharp for you add more.

If you suffer from cold hands and feet, you may have a predisposition to arthritis, in which case you should have this drink every day. A friend who was prone to migraine attacks drinks this mixture twice a day and has not had an attack for years since she started taking it.

Honey should not be given to infants under a year old.

Fresh Vegetables and Fruit

There is no doubt that if our diet contained some fresh vegetables and fruit every day, there would be a marked increase in our health. The difficulty is to get them really fresh, and, if the result of the rise in prices is to turn us all back into a nation of vegetable gardeners, we shall derive considerable benefit.

If you have a deep freeze, it is well worth growing your own – especially the less familiar vegetables which do so much to lift a meal into the gourmet class and which are never cheap. Any gardening book will tell you the best varieties for freezing.

Even without this, however, it is worth growing things which will keep in store (notably, apples and onions) and carrots will keep well in dry sand.

Even if you have no garden at all, it is now possible to grow tomatoes (full sized fruits on miniature plants) on a window sill or balcony, and, of course, as many herbs as your window box will accommodate. Not only do these add interest to your diet but all contain valuable nutrients and trace elements – in other words, they are 'real' food.

Shopping for Value

Specialist stores are usually dearer than the ordinary grocers and, provided it is pure, there is no reason why honey, for instance, should not be bought at an ordinary grocers. However, you should not grudge the extra pennies that you may be asked to pay for the whole foods which are obtainable at the specialist stores as they will prove to be an economy in the long run because you will find that you need less in order to satisfy your nutritional requirements. Some of the foods which were until recently only obtainable at the specialist stores have become so popular that they are now obtainable anywhere. Muesli is the obvious example. Here, however, the Health Food Stores will prove to be cheaper than the grocers because you can obtain from them muesli base to which you can add your own fruit and nuts. You should look out for wholemeal flour and speciality breads in the local grocers where they may be cheaper than in the specialist stores.

There is much satisfaction as well as economy in making some of these things yourself, notably bread, yogurt, cream and muesli.

Sprouting Seeds

It is now possible to obtain many types of seeds for sprouting. The sprouts or shoots are delicious and nutritious and the process of sprouting is simplicity itself. You do not need any special equipment – a large jam jar, a piece of muslin or similar material to go over the top and neck of the jar and a rubber band to secure it there. Into the jar you put a dessertspoonful of your chosen seed, rinse it round with ordinary cold water (in winter, you can just take the chill off it, to aid germination of the seeds), secure the muslin and let the water drain out through it. Put the jar on its side so that it will continue to drain, in a shaded place. Repeat the rinsing night and morning. You will find you can pour the water through the muslin and need not take it off the jar. In three to six days, depending on the type of seeds, you will have your sprouts, which can then be eaten raw, or cooked for just a few minutes in boiling water, so that they remain crisp. The most popular seeds are as follows:

Alfalfa. These are very fine seeds and the sprouts are fully grown in three days. They taste rather like new pea pods and are best eaten raw.

Mung Beans. These are familiar to most of us as Chinese beansprouts. The sprouts will take six days to develop fully. These are delicious raw or cooked.

Fenugreek/Herbal Green Mint Sprouts. Both of these have a very distinctive flavour and are nice to combine with other sprouts for a mixed salad.

All are full of essential minerals and vitamins and make a most useful winter salad when other raw vegetables are not available.

A Bonus For Your Looks

At the moment, there is a great vogue in the use of natural ingredients in the cosmetic industry. Despite the advertisements telling us of the benefits to our skin of avocado, cucumber and many other fruits and vegetables, many health experts tell us that none of the creams with which we anoint our skin are capable of penetrating. The situation is quite different when the fruits and vegetables are taken as food. The bonus from eating natural foods, in terms of beauty, is youthful looks. Shining hair, good colour, clear skin and surplus energy are well worth having when they are obtained for so little expenditure of time and energy in buying the best. An added zest for life and healthy old age will be your reward for making sure that the foods you eat are both natural and delicious.

Whole Food Value Chart (In Percentages)

	Protein	Carbohydrate	Fat	Calories per oz (25g)
Wholemeal Bread	7	48	–	63
Pearl Barley	7.8	83	1.8	102
Bran	14	58	3.8	92
Brazil Nuts	13.6	8	70	210
Brown Sugar	–	97	–	114
Butter	–	0.5	84	223
Cheddar Cheese	27	–	33	120
Dried Fruits:				
Apple	1.1	58	0.6	71
Apricots	5.5	47.6	0.2	60
Currants	1.6	56	–	68
Dates(Stoned)	1.9	64.3	–	74
Figs	2.7	55	–	65

	Protein	Carbohydrate	Fat	Calories per oz (25g)
Prunes	2.3	37	–	44
Raisins & Sultanas	1.8	60	–	71
Hazelnuts	13.1	14.1	63	199
Honey	3.5	76.5	–	82
Milk (Low Fat)	36	63.2	–	102
81% Flour	11.1	73.8	1.6	96
Muesli	12	67	8	107
Oatmeal	12	71	9	114
Rice (Natural)	7.5	77	1.7	102
Rye Flour	6	81	2	105
Fruit Juices				
Tomato Juice	1.23	2.37	–	6
Apple Juice	0.05	11.2	–	13
Grape Juice	10.3	15-18	–	21
Walnuts	13.8	13.9	66	207
Wheat Germ (Stabilised)	23	55	8.4	107
Wheat Germ (Natural)	28	40	10	101
Wholemeal Pasta (Macaroni, Spaghetti, etc.)	13.5	68.5	3.2	101
Wholewheat	11.9	71.2	1.8	94

Nature Cure

Nature Cure has been described as 'a philosophy of living to maintain health',* rather than an annual 'cure' and, in the main, it comprises a life style which includes eating only the natural foods which have already been described. The proportions of each type of food are given as follows: 75 per cent should be alkaline foods, which are cleansing to the blood stream and organs. These might well consist of one-third raw salad vegetables (leaves and roots), one-third fresh fruit (or dried substitutes, if well-soaked) and one-third of cooked leaf and root vegetables.

* *Nature Cure in a Nutshell* by Tom W. Moule, ND (Thorsons, 1953)

25 per cent of foods which nourish, but which are also acid-forming, as to roughly two-fifths protein (fish, meat, eggs, cheese and nuts), two-fifths carbohydrate (cereals, grains and unsoaked dried fruits, honey or molasses) and one-fifth fats (butter, margarine, nut fats and animal fats).

This is the ideal and is not always attainable. In conditions of ill-health, one or other of the categories may need to be increased or decreased. Tension and overwork 'eat up' protein and this will need to be replaced, so that the proteins may need to form 25 per cent of each day's food. The real danger to avoid is an excess of starch food and an increase in this is only permissable for those doing really hard physical work.

Some people find it difficult to assimilate the minerals which they require in the form of food, or they use up more of one than another, and it is then helpful to take specially prepared tissue salts (see page 47). In addition, some of the vitamins are easily lost in food preparation or if the food is not completely fresh, and vitamin supplements can then be helpful. However, if you are getting good quality food in the correct proportions, such supplements should not be necessary.

Nature Cure maintains, rightly, I believe, that health is the normal state and the body itself is a wonderful regulator and healer, which does not usually require help if a person is eating and living sensibly

However, its practitioners are prepared to offer treatments to help toxic conditions caused by the accumulation of waste products (largely due to the wrong type of eating). In the main, these consist of going on to a rigid programme of dieting for up to three weeks at a time, helped by various types of baths to stimulate the skin to throw off the toxic conditions. They also recommend colonic irrigation and enemas.

Allergies

It would appear that allergic diseases are not normally self-induced and that they can affect any of the zodiacal types.

While Capricorn is the obvious candidate for skin troubles, it seems that sensitive skins are often a hereditary feature. Certainly, from a Capricorn Sun-sign mother both of my sisters (Cancer and Libra) and myself (Pisces) have inherited this, but of course, not all skin troubles are due to allergies – often they are the result of wrong diet and can also be psychosomatic.

Allergies can range from house dust to pollen, as many hay-fever sufferers know to their cost, to many ingredients of ordinary household articles, soap, cleansers and cosmetics.

However, the work of Professor Selye and others have high-lighted the fact that some of us are allergic to certain types of food and these are not always the ones we would naturally suspect. While it is true that over-refined sugar is toxic to all of us, who would suspect milk or eggs – the traditional diet for the treatment of tuberculosis?

Dr Richard Mackarness in his book *Not all in the Mind* has cited many cases where wrong diet (wrong for that particular person) has not only caused physical illnesses of lesser or greater degree – ranging from catarrh to cancer – but also mental illnesses. In some cases these are severe enough for the patient to be confined in a psychiatric hospital for years with symptoms ranging from deep depression to violence, including self-inflicted wounds.

Although it is only recently that diet allergies have been suspected in these cases, it is many years since experiments have proved that chronic ailments like colitis, eczema and migraine could be cured by removing eggs, milk, chocolate and other common foods from the sufferer's diet. Wheat and gluten and, indeed, all cereals can be poison to some people, while most of us can happily adapt to a wide range of foods.

Nor is there any danger for the majority of us in doing so – provided that the food has not been contaminated by chemicals used in spraying, aluminium in wrapping or by the addition of non-food flavouring and preservatives (all of which can cause their own problems).

For those who suffer from chronic illnesses *for which no cause has been discovered after all the usual medical tests*, it now seems sensible to suspect items in the normal diet.

Most of us are well aware of the foods which invariably upset us and refrain from eating them. These foods do not come into that category. Their effect is hidden because the patient often feels better immediately after eating them.

The problem is bound up with the subject of stress. If we consider a situation in which a stress is suddenly inflicted on us and then continues for some time, we realise that our first reaction is panic and distress followed by adaptation to the continuing situation. Often the better we appear to adapt the more violent our sudden collapse may be after the prolonged period of stress which has exhausted our reserves of strength. In the same way, the body will adapt to a food which is rejected violently in childhood. A parent will say, 'He couldn't drink milk as a baby, but I persevered and he has no trouble now', little realising that the stress on the body is only being supressed and will eventually show itself in some form, but without indicating that the food is at fault.

There are also similar symptoms to that of addiction. The food is one that the patient enjoys and eats frequently. The symptoms of his complaint seem to be helped by eating that particular item and the patient suffers if he is deprived of it. It follows, therefore, that the last thing that he suspects is that this particular food could be the cause of his chronic illness.

Doctor Mackarness advocates a diet of plain water for five days before trying the suspected food to see whether it will produce an immediate reaction. If the symptoms of the illness continue during the five-day diet then food is not the cause of the illness. This is obviously a good way to ascertain whether one particular item of diet is causing trouble, but it would take a very long time to test more than one (and often there are several foods which are suspect).

Before I describe the work of Brian Butler who has largely solved this problem, I would emphasise again that most people can take a wide variety of foods and it is in their interest to do so, since they are then sure of getting all the vitamins and trace elements that they need. Dr Mackarness himself is an advocate of a diet based on largely meat and fat. I have just been listening to a talk where a doctor is advocating more fibre and no fat so that it is obvious that the experts do not agree among themselves. In these circumstances it seems wise for the layman to take responsibility for his own diet and find out for himself what it is that his own body requires.

I became a vegetarian when I had a problem with high blood pressure. Three months later, it was back to normal. Obviously, it was the right decision for me, but we are all individuals and need to find out what suits our own body best.

Cholesterol is the 'in' thing in the USA as I write. Many people there who do not know their blood pressure know their cholesterol level. We know that it is a substance made by the body and that over-production causes many health problems, but we do not yet know what factors cause over-production. While it is sensible to limit the intake of high cholesterol in accordance with present knowledge, do not increase your blood pressure by worrying about it!

Alistair Cooke tells of an American who is eating two dozen eggs a day. Doctors are puzzled because he has *low* cholesterol. He is a compulsive egg eater and commented, 'These damned eggs are ruining my life.' He is 88 years old.

Kinesiology

Kinesiology is based on the book by Dr John Thie called *Touch for Health*. He founded the 'Touch for Health Foundation' in America and many instructors have been trained there. In England there are a growing number and Mr Butler is one of the few full-time instructors. He looks upon himself as an educator rather than a therapist, since the work that he does is mainly teaching people how to look after themselves. In an interview with me he explained the science of muscle testing.

This is a means of finding out where the imbalances in the body lie and also defines what is causing such imbalances.

He said that the matter is considered at the mental level which includes the psychological, emotional and spiritual make up, the physical level relating to the structure of muscles and bones, etc., and the chemical level which describes the organs and the biochemistry of the body and includes the digestion of food and the elimination of toxins.

Part of the diagnostic of using muscle testing is to determine whether the imbalance is a nutritional problem, energy imbalance, muscular imbalance or whether (as is usual) there is a psychosomatic component.

Mr Butler says,

The wonderful thing about muscle testing is that it is instantaneous in the pinpointing of trouble from a food. All the different muscle groups in the body are related to different organs and one in the chest is linked to the stomach function and can be used to determine whether any given substance is reactive to that person.

I use the word 'reactive' advisedly because I distinguish between the allergic and the reaction which is not apparent or readily visible. Immediate reaction after eating is allergic but the problem of eating reactive food is that over a longer period of time it tires the body. It leads to the exhaustion of the adrenals and then the nerves get ragged, the body's defence against toxins becomes impaired and the defence mechanism against the invasion of proteins becomes much reduced.

He feels that, although symptoms must be dealt with, prevention is most important: 'People are defensive about their own life style and it is the life style which produces the problems we have. Therefore, this style must be changed and people tend to be resistant to this.'

Dr John Thie believes that it should be part of everyone's basic education to look after themselves and says that 'Touch for Health' classes offer people sane, practical, down-to-earth approaches to diet, exercise, muscle and energy balancing and taking an intelligent interest in the way the body works so that they can help themselves and their own families to stay in a better balanced state.

Although, of course, people must be advised to seek professional help for persistent problems there is no reason why they should not be encouraged to take some degree of responsibility for their own health.

To test for a reactive food is very simple. The person extends the left arm at an angle of 90° to the body, directly in front of them, so that there is also a 90° angle between the arm and the floor, with the thumb pointing towards the floor.

This turns the arm in an apparently awkward way. Then the person who is testing gently holds the subject by his right shoulder in order to stabilise him, and uses the right hand to press on the subject's wrist just above the joint of the extended left arm, down onto the top of the wrist and away from the body, with a steady firm pressure for about two seconds only.

The purpose of this initial test is to determine whether the muscle is functioning properly in the first place. If it is painful or very weak this muscle would have to be strengthened before one could proceed.

If the subject's muscle is normally strong, any substance can now be introduced to the mouth. It does not have to be swallowed – for best results it should be chewed and can then be discarded. While in the mouth, the test is done again to see if the subject can still resist the same pressure on the wrist. Any change at all indicates the the food is less than beneficial to the body to some degree. The greater the reaction, the greater the degree to which that substance is adversely affecting the body. A substance which is very bad for that particular person will probably mean that the muscle will not hold up against the gentle pressure of one finger instead of the normal firm pressure of three fingers.

It takes only a few seconds and the mouth only needs to be rinsed out between each test, so that twenty or thirty substances can be tested in a few minutes. It is, however, necessary not to overtire the subject or overstrain the muscle.

This simple technique can be learned by anyone, but it takes practice and must be done sensitively and with care. Mr Butler has taught over 1000 people now, including children. He finds that the thing which intrigues and excites them most is that they get immediate feedback from the body as to what is suitable. It is also possible to find out which foods are actively good and these can be used to strengthen the muscles.

Exercise and Relaxation

If the body is to be completely healthy, it needs correct diet, fresh air, exercise and rest. Every one of these basic necessities is at risk in the world in which we live. We have already looked at diet, and I do not intend to say a great deal about exercise. I have mentioned the ones most likely to appeal to each zodiacal type under its own sign. However, some kinds of exercise are also relaxations – yoga, eurhythmy, gardening and walking can all help to disperse tensions and can do nothing but good. Other exercises are combative, tension-forming and competitive. They will tone up the muscles, including the heart muscles, and generally help the physical body to stay fit, but if they are not followed by relaxation they may build their own tensions (especially mental ones if the exercise has been over-exciting) and the mind and body then go short of the rest which they need. In relation to exercise, I would remind you of a quotation from yoga. 'Enough is enough, but enough is necessary.'

Exercises for Everyone

As we get older it becomes increasingly important that mobility should be maintained. Here are some exercises which only take a few minutes to do each morning. If you get into the habit of doing them you will increase your chances of retaining freedom of movement right until the end of your life.

None of these should be done strenuously. Do not force them and only do what you are able to accomplish without strain. As you continue to do them you will find that your mobility increases and you may be able to do more than the suggested amount.

Before rising in the morning: Exercise 1

Laying flat on your back in bed, bend one knee up to your chest (or as far as it will go). Do not strain to the point where it hurts. You are not going in for competition, but only trying to maintain and perhaps improve the mobility you already have. Count five and lower your leg. Repeat with the other leg. Relax.

Now bring both knees up to the chest slowly. Lift both legs at a right angle to the body or as far as is comfortable. Lower the legs slowly on to the bed. This is a good exercise for the stomach muscles. It is also what our American cousins call, 'a good de-gasser' to relieve flatulence and expel 'windy' pains.

Exercise 2

Lift one leg from the bed to a comfortable angle, supporting it with your clasped hands. Slowly rotate the ankle to the left seven times. If you find this difficult start with less and gradually work up to seven – or ten if you feel like it. Now rotate to the right in the same way. Lower the leg and repeat with the other leg.

On rising: Exercise 1

Standing straight, roll your shoulders forwards seven times. Relax. Roll them back seven times. Again, if you find resistance, start with fewer rotations and work up to seven. If you do a job which tires your back and shoulder muscles, try to remember to do this at intervals through the day. It also helps to do general shoulder movements, shrugging and so on.

Exercise 2

Standing straight, stretch your arms out sideways. Keeping your arms straight flap your wrists – up to twenty times. You may not get 'lift off' but you will certainly get the adrenalin flowing. You can do this exercise quite energetically.

Exercise 3

Standing straight with your arms at your sides, turn you head to the left, drop the head and rotate your head over your chest and to the right side. Repeat from right to left. Do this two or three times.

I guarantee that these exercises will not take more than five minutes. I do them every morning and I never have more than that amount of time to spare.

These are all good exercises to repeat during the day as you have the opportunity to do so. Even the ankle rotating exercises do not require you to lie flat every time – you can do them merely sitting down.

If you never get any other exercise during the day, I do most strongly urge that you should get at least this amount.

Deep Breathing

The importance of this can hardly be exaggerated. The introduction of air into the lungs stimulates the blood flow and will prevent it becoming sluggish. If it is flowing normally it will wash away the calcium deposits which may otherwise build up on the joints, especially on the fingers, giving the characteristic appearance of arthritis. Those who suffer from cold hands and feet may have a tendency to arthritis and rheumatism and can help to stop these troubles developing by doing some deep breathing night and morning.

Another advantage of such a practice is that it helps to wake you up in the mornings and relaxes you at night. You should wear loose-fitting clothes and sit or stand comfortably while you breathe in for a count of two and then expel *all* the air in your lungs. (There is always more than you think and I usually find myself making some strange groaning noises as I get to the end!) Then breathe in for a count of three and repeat. Gradually work up to a count of ten, by increasing by one on each occasion. If you get at all dizzy, then just do as much as you can, but most people will manage ten with no difficulty.

Most physical tension begins in the mind so methods of relaxing the mind need to be found and in this connection I would particularly like to consider Meditation and Bio-feedback.

Meditation

It is very difficult to make the mind a blank, so thoughts which cause tension need to be replaced by soothing ones.

I have taught many people to relax by the simple method of closing their eyes, taking a few deep breaths and imagining themselves into a scene which they know they will find relaxing. For some, this will be a country walk, for others a seascape or a walk round a beautiful garden. Whatever they choose, they must feel themselves to be there – hear the birds singing, the waves breaking, smell the perfume of the flowers... If you practise this, and can take your mind away to that enchanted place for ten minutes, or as long as you can spare, you will find tensions dropping away from you. This is a type of meditation in its simplest form.

There are now many Schools of Meditation, all of which have their own techniques and some of which are directed towards one particular spiritual path. This is not the place to describe them but you should have no difficulty in finding out what is on offer.

Bio-feedback

We are familiar with the term 'feedback'. It simply means that we get information coming back to us from other people as a result of the information or projects which we have discussed with them. They tell us their views on the subject and this enables us to reconsider and perhaps modify our future actions in respect of that subject.

A tennis player, for instance, will get feedback from his coach and perhaps also from video film to enable him to correct faults in his play.

Bio-feedback is getting this sort of information from our own bodies. We can be connected to machines which will measure our heart beats or pulse rates, the warmth of our bodies and even the amount of tension in the brain. It has been discovered that, with such information, a man can slow down his pulse rate at will, warm or cool any part of his body and, most importantly to our subject, reduce mental tension and permit his mind to relax.

A small meter strapped to the wrist and causing no more discomfort than a wrist watch will monitor the brain waves as they pass from Beta – wideawake active waves – to Alpha (a pleasant relaxed condition), to Theta – a meditative state of consciousness where original creativity is sometimes a by-product. Delta waves usually occur only in deep sleep.

Even those who find it difficult to relax can usually achieve alpha waves quite quickly, simply by concentrating on relaxing enough to get the meter into the alpha waveband. Once the technique has been learned, the meter can be discarded – the client now knows how to relax and will not forget it.

This technique has been found effective in curing migraine and tension headaches, reducing high blood-pressure and insomnia and restoring control to damaged muscles. In this country, its applications have yet to be used to the full.

Having experienced it myself, I believe it will prove to be a valuable technique for a great many people; the exceptions are likely to be those who become too obsessed with watching the machines instead of using them for their proper purpose.

Spiritual Health

Over many years of experience, I have come to the conclusion that there is no bodily health without spiritual health. By this I do not mean to imply that we should have reached a certain standard of 'goodness' but that we should be aware of being on a spiritual path – a journey towards a goal.

If we are not conscious of this – our beliefs and our ultimate goal – we shall lose our 'way' and our physical health will be affected by a false sense of the futility of life. What is it all about? Is anything worth doing? are questions we all ask at some stage in our lives. If, at such a time, a series of unfortunate events occur, such as we all experience occasionally, this may take the ground from under our feet and we go down into what is called 'nervous breakdown', but which is really a spiritual crisis. The apparent futility of effort, at a time when all efforts and decisions have turned out to be the wrong ones (to our restricted view) may even make us suicidal, and, at best, take all the joy out of life.

It is for this reason, I believe, that various psychological therapies, directing us to take charge of our own lives are having such a vogue, especially in America, but increasingly in Europe also. Some of these therapies are valuable tools. We outgrow old beliefs, but fail to update them, and we all know those who need to come out from the shadow of others and find their own self-esteem. It is right that we should value ourselves, since we are all 'temples of the Living God' but the ego-centred existence carries its own dangers – one, among many, being to cut us off from the joys of giving. There is a path we must tread between being only concerned with our own growth and being over-concerned for others. Truly has it been described as a 'narrow way'. The ego-centred path, if followed to the extreme, eventually cuts us off from other human contact and it is surely still true that 'every man's death diminishes me, for I am involved in mankind'.

Beliefs are very personal and no-one can formulate them for anyone else, but if there is one thing that both astrology and history teach us it is that there is *no end* – either to life or to opportunity. As Lyall Watson pointed out in *The Romeo Error*, living matter may change into something else but it does not cease to exist. Mankind has survived incredible odds, civilisations have been cast down and new ones have arisen, and in our own personal lives we are presented with our opportunities not once, but many times, if our eyes are only open to them. We have all known people who thought they were too old at thirty to achieve something and other people of seventy and older who are branching out into new fields of experience. In our own country, the start of the Open University saw many mature people seize the opportunity to study for degrees in all kinds of subjects and to prove triumphantly that age is no bar to achievement. How many of them must have thought when they left school that the opportunity of taking a degree had passed them by for ever.

'You never know what's round the corner' was a favourite expression of my grandmother's when anyone was downcast, and this is exactly what the study of astrology tells us. The planets move endlessly, in a never-repeating pattern, yet as each transits the significant areas of our own birth charts they bring us challenge and opportunities – a never-ending stream.

It is said that a great man once asked for a motto that would give him hope in time of despair and prevent him from over-elation in times of great happiness and the motto suggested was 'It will pass'. True as this is, I would rather take as my motto 'It will come' – for everything does, in the fullness of time.

The soul needs – hungers for – opportunities for personal growth and if these are denied it dies for want of its natural food. How can the body be healthy if it lacks the life of the spirit?

My own approach to astrology is shared by many other astrologers. I believe that we reincarnate many times in order to learn all our lessons and that the birth chart is a good guide to our path for this life. So my reply to 'what are we here for' would be – to learn, to grow ever more whole (which is the same word as 'holy') and in that belief we can welcome all experiences, good and bad, as a means to an end. Moreover, each new experience widens our horizon – to quote Tennyson, 'All experience is an arch, where thro' gleams that untravelled world, whose margin fades for ever and for ever, as I move.'

I have no wish to impose my own belief on my readers, but I have included a suggestion for their own spiritual path for each zodiacal type, in the hope that some may find help from it. Generally, what is right psychologically is also right spiritually, so that if, for instance, your are a Water type who tends to be overconcerned with others, psychologically you need to cultivate a certain amount of detachment, to value yourself more and to find relief from worrying by finding peace within yourself, and in doing this you also find the spiritual path which is right for you.

To those who think it strange that I should write of spiritual values in a book on 'astrology and health' I can only say that perfect health encompasses the wholeness of body, mind and spirit.

THE ZODIACAL SIGNS

Introduction

Most of us are aware of the zodiacal sign in which the Sun was situated at our time of birth. Newspaper 'astrology' refers to those people born between 20 March and 19 April as Aries, and such people will often tell others 'I'm an Arien' without realising that this is what is meant – that the Sun was in that part of the heavens which astrologers call Aries.

The Sun position is an important feature of our birth charts, but it is by no means the only factor, and sometimes it is not even the most important one. The Moon and all the planets are somewhere in the chart and so is an important point known as the Ascendant (the sign and degree rising on the eastern horizon at the time and place of birth).

If you do not know your own birth chart, you should read through all the descriptions which follow and decide what is relevant to you, in terms of health. If you know where your Moon, Ascendant and ruling planet fall, you should read the descriptions under each of these signs. Also consider the placing of Mars for vitality.

It is just because the birth chart is so complicated that you will rarely find everything applying to you in the description of any one sign, so keep an open mind about the suggestions given and adapt them to suit yourself. You may find, for instance, that although you have a Sagittarian Sun sign, you are doing the sort of physical work described under Virgo which results in certain strains that require the treatment suggested for Virgo's aches and pains.

The type of exercise suggested may not be possible for you. This is not an excuse for doing nothing! Find a substitute of the same kind which appeals to you. It has been impossible to mention all the many types available.

Many treatments are applicable to everyone. Just because they are not mentioned specifically for your sign, this does not mean they are unsuitable. It is surely worth while for perfect health to take a little trouble to find a technique, and a practitioner, suitable to you. Again, it has not been possible to mention all the therapies available, but the book list will introduce you to others, and the magazines devoted to health will contain addresses you can write to for further information.

Each of the zodiacal signs is somewhere in your birth chart, even though it may not be emphasised by having a planet in it. In order to be 'whole' people, we really need to try to balance the characteristics of all the signs within ourselves. Naturally we will be more inclined towards some characteristics than to others, and this statement may sound like nonsense on first reading. However, if we begin by considering each sign in turn as showing a stage of a journey through a life, the pattern will emerge clearly.

In Aries, we see the coming forth into life – the dawn of civilisation. At that stage, the will to live is the necessary characteristic and everything that is life-enhancing is relevant.

Having survived, we must now consolidate. Taurus turns us to the practicalities – till the soil, cultivate, and build shelters. Everything which relates to the nourishing and protection of the body is emphasised together with all the physical aspects of life on earth. Patience and persistence are necessary to achieve basic physical comforts.

The Gemini stage is intellectual activity, which implies communication with others and learning all manner of things. This covers the whole range from mere gossip to tuition. It also emphasises movement, which can be aimless running around in search of new sensations or voyages of exploration.

Now the developing community is based on the home. In Cancer we see the home-maker, who is also the Universal Mother-protector and nurturer of the weaker ones. In this sign also patriotism and a growing pride in nationality leads inevitably to the next stage.

A king, or leader, comes to power by the will of the people. He signifies order and organisation and he is able to dignify the nation by his office. The kingly quality is also shown in breadth of vision. He seeks the good of the greatest number and has ceased to become wholly concerned with himself. It is represented by Leo.

Kingship implies subjects – and these are the Virgoans. These people are willing to offer service to the community without self seeking. They are typified in the ordinary working people of a country.

We now have a stable community, and from this point on people are free to turn their attention to other matters. In the sign of Libra, we first have an emphasis on relationships to other people. Here tact and diplomacy are called for, together with an appreciation of more than one point of view. Librans are called upon to realise that other people's plans and ideas are just as valid as their own, and it is at this stage that the concept of justice is born.

In Scorpio there is an ever increasing desire to penetrate to the very depths in exploration of nature's secrets and in a deeper understanding of others. The amount of forcefulness which is present in the Scorpionic nature can be liberating or destructive. Sagittarius turns the mind to philosophy and the laws which are life-expanding and enhancing, freeing us from bondages which we may have created for ourselves by the rigidity of our former beliefs and opinions. This influence carried to extremes can dissolve all boundaries and can be just as damaging as rigidity.

The Capricorn characteristic awakens ambition and provides the necessary perseverance to achieve our goals. The higher our aims (in the spiritual sense) the more Capricorn will enable us to attain. Purely worldly goals can bring their own problems.

The Aquarian has no time for hypocrisy, false ideals or unjust laws but may seek to change them by overthrowing law and order rather than by more peaceful means.

With the advent of Pisces we have the mystic who is already half in a higher world. His search can lead him to great truths and high aspirations, but lack of practicality may instead lead him into a world of illusions.

From this trip round the zodiac you will see that life's lessons gradually involve us all in developing each of the characteristics to a greater or lesser degree. You can also see that each can be over-stressed and can cause problems. This will be even more apparent as we examine each sign separately.

A great deal of our time is spent in working and work (or work conditions) for which a person is not suited can cause many tensions, leading to ill health. It is always worthwhile to give much thought to the matter of a career and also to take stock of your general life style at intervals throughout your life, to see what effect it may be having on your health. You may find options open to you which you would not have considered but for this stock-taking.

The analyses of each of the zodiacal signs have been written to help you to do just this.

Aries

The Sun is in this sign from about 20 March to 19 April, depending on the year and time of day when you were born. You may also be considered an Aries type if you have an Aries Ascendant, or if the Moon or Mars were in this sign at the time of your birth. Mars is said to be the ruler of Aries, and if it is in its own sign you are likely to be strongly Arien in character even if your Sun sign is elsewhere in the chart.

Aries is a Fire sign and, combined with the Martian energy, it makes the Arien a vital, dynamic personality. He is usually quick and active and the over abundance of vitality makes it very difficult for him to slow down. He is a pioneering type – stimulated by danger, keen at being first at all times, and he enjoys starting new ventures. His enthusiasm is stimulating to others and he is a good leader. He may erupt quickly – into action or passion, but tempers are soon forgotten – life is too short and there are other adventures calling him.

He has a good brain, but is inclined to act first and think afterwards. His mind is rarely at rest (any more than the body) and he is always full of new ideas to try out.

As a child, he is likely to appear utterly selfish as he is only concerned with his own affairs. This is nothing but thoughtlessness, as he is just the person to make sacrifices for others when he is aware of their needs.

Because of the self-orientation, the Arien is quite likely to make mountains out of molehills if anything trivial is wrong with him, basically because it stops him getting on with life and is an annoyance. His courage is legendary however and serious physical disabilities are bravely met and largely ignored while he gets on with what he really wants to do.

Unfortunately we cannot all be leaders and many Ariens are bound to find themselves in subordinate positions and in boring repetitive work where little initiative is required. This is likely to generate mental tension which needs to be released in hobbies, exercise or other part-time work. It is worth taking considerable trouble to find a congenial position, preferably where there is an ultimate goal and where the circumstances are challenging. The Arien's drive and power really need to be used in a position of leadership if he is to feel completely fulfilled, and if this cannot be found in his working life he should seek for it in other activities.

Ariens rarely suffer from the types of ill health which are caused by psychological difficulties, as they do not brood over things and are not often over concerned about relationships with others. Being ruled by Mars, their vitality is also likely to be above average. This sounds as though it should be a blessing, but it is not an unmixed one. Ariens tend to overtax themselves simply because they have an abundance of energy. They are also prone to accidents because of their quick movements, a tendency to rush into things (literally not looking where they are going) and, generally, in over-estimating their physical power to cope with all the demands that an active brain can put upon them. Thus burns, bruises and cuts are commonplace things to an Arien. A conscious effort to slow down will reduce these and help them to be more relaxed.

The Arien desperately needs some of the balance of his opposite sign Libra and if he wishes to remain in perfect health he should make sure that he gets mental as well as physical relaxation. He needs to learn to know when and where to stop and not to dissipate his energy by trying to do everything twice as fast as anyone else. His time should be balanced between activity and relaxation.

As regards diet, the Arien needs dairy products, honey, nuts, sunflower and sesame seeds, tomatoes, beetroot (grated raw), lemons, grapefruit and celery (see also Tissue Salts).

Any physical exercise is suitable for the Arien, especially those which call for co-ordination of body and mind. He will excel as a team leader and enjoy the more dangerous sports.

As a relaxation, he should practise Bio-feedback techniques.

The parts of the body ruled by Aries are the head, the cerebral system and the adrenal glands. Apart from accidents, he may suffer from headaches and migraine, eye, nose and ear infections, feverish conditions and vertigo, head colds and neuralgia. He may also suffer from dental troubles.

A daily drink of honey and cider vinegar (two teaspoonsful of each in a glass of water) will help migraine conditions and keep his system toned up. Headaches may be caused by sluggish kidney action (see Libra).

Ariens are likely to react positively to acupuncture, reflexology and massage (a brisk massage followed by a relaxing one).

For first aid, the Arien should keep Calendula tincture, Arnica (tablets and cream), *Hepar. Sulph.* to assist the healing of wounds, and *Rhus. Tox.* tincture for sprains, and Euphrasia tincture for the eyes, in the Homoeopathic remedies. In the Bach flower remedies, Rescue, Rock Rose or Star of Bethlehem should be available in emergencies. For longer-term treatment keep the Tissue Salt *Kali. Phos.* and the Bach flower remedy, Impatiens.

Herbs which are helpful to Aries people are:

Dandelion, which contains *Kali. Phos.*, the salt which Ariens are usually lacking, also for kidney disorders.

Basil for healing wounds.

Balm for all feverish complaints.

Bergamot to help mental relaxation.

Borage for the adrenal system and kidneys, also for fevers. It is particularly valuable when energy has been depleted through over activity.

Comfrey for the rapid healing of broken bones or sprains, also as a cold compress for eye injuries.

Eyebright for eye troubles, though it is probably more convenient to have it in the homoeopathic tincture and tablets (see Euphrasia).

Elderberry for fevers and to soothe burns and scalds. Feverfew should be taken regularly to prevent migraine, if this is a problem.

Thyme is good for fevers and inflamed wounds, also for headaches, migraine and kidney troubles.

Chamomile for external use for neuralgia, toothache and ear ache.

Ginseng for mental exhaustion and as a general tonic.

Hyssop for external use for bruises and cuts.

Lavender for headaches and migraine.

Witch Hazel to check bleeding (as ointment or liquid).

For Ariens, psychological and spiritual health can be described in the word 'balance'. The need to project themselves is an obsessive one and usually takes up all their energy. They are all extrovert, and although their brains may be very active they never give themselves time to think where their headlong rush is leading them. Because of the tension which this sort of life engenders, illness may strike them down very suddenly. If it is disabling, so that they are brought to a sudden halt, the psychological effect can be very traumatic.

While it is not suggested that they should abrogate their capacity for leadership, it is important (both psychologically and spiritually) that they should recognise the rights and the worth of other people. All the Fire signs are inclined to set themselves apart from (and above) others even if they do not make it obvious. The Arien does not suffer fools gladly but a little more humility might teach him that the fools had something to offer and would certainly help him to appreciate his fellow human beings more. He feels self-sufficient until the day arrives when he really needs others – and that is a feeling with which he simply cannot cope. Aries is perhaps the most masculine of the signs (certainly it is the bravest) and in such a condition the Arien feels emasculated. He needs to reach out to others, giving them the same respect which he gives himself. In this way, he becomes a whole, rounded person, instead of the one-pointed, self-obsessed character which is the typical Arien. Luckily most of us are a more balanced mixture, as shown by the various signs which the planets occupy in our charts, but if you are more Arien than anything, may I suggest a motto 'Slow down to keep your balance'.

Taurus

The Sun is in the sign of Taurus from about 20 April to 20 May, but you can also be considered a Taurean type if you have the moon or Venus in Taurus, or if Taurus is rising in the birth chart (in the Ascendant).

This is an Earth sign which is ruled by the planet Venus. Like all the Earth signs the Taurean has his feet firmly on the ground and is practical. However, he also has the sensitivity bestowed by the rulership of Venus which makes him creative and an art and nature lover.

Despite this rulership, Taurus is the most 'earthy' of the Earth signs. He is concerned with physical matter – that which we can touch, build with and shape. He values material possessions and his creature comforts.

Sensory gratification is important to him, and this is permissible as long as it does not become an end in itself. Like Mother Earth herself, the Taurean nourishes life and is a producer, liking to leave his mark on the world in concrete form.

He has a great sense of values and this attracts him to things of beauty and intrinsic worth and also to the world of finance. The best type of Taurean has stability, together with tolerance and warmth. He is dependable and, like the other Earth sign of Capricorn, he will get there in his own good time and he illustrates the sheer power of endurance (like the Bull that is the symbol of his birth month). He enjoys taking his time to do things properly and his unhurried efforts materialise in well-built houses, tidy and productive gardens and beautifully proportioned craftsmanship of all kinds.

He is not easily ruffled and is restful to be with, except when he has been goaded too far and then he can literally be like a bull in a china shop. His practicality instinctively picks out the essentials. His relationships are enduring as he is faithful and a good friend.

The dangers to his health lie in the over stress of his natural characteristics, so that he can become lazy and self-indulgent, ruining his health by too little exercise and too much pleasure.

He needs security and the reassurance of love and because of these basic needs he can be both possessive of people and rather mean. He is obstinate and tends to resist change, and, in fact, feels greatly disturbed by changing conditions. His great love of nature is an important part of his attitude to health. The contact helps to revitalise him almost as though he drew his energy from the earth. It follows that to be truly healthy, the Taurean needs to renew his links with nature – either in the form of gardening or walking in the country whenever possible.

While he is often drawn to an artistic vocation, he would need to feel that it was a safe one and so he often opts for a practical career, keeping his artistic work as a relaxing hobby. He is very good at handling finance and is often found in related careers. At the same time, he much enjoys the type of work where he is designing and constructing something, so that he eventually has a finished product. Like all the Earth signs, he likes to see concrete results and careers of this type bring together the artistic and practical sides of his nature. He should never go into a career which is likely to be a gamble. That would worry him far too much.

The Venusian influence makes him a connoisseur of the good things of life, food, wine and a comfortable home. And of course he is also a lover of all bodily comforts.

While there is no reason why anybody should become ill, all zodiacal types have a tendency to some diseases more than others. In the Taurean the troubles are likely to arise from throat infections, bronchitis, goitre, over-weight conditions caused by a tendency to retain fluid, diseases involving the neck, asthma and sinusitis. He needs to avoid obesity, and to make sure that he gets plenty of active exercise. The kidneys are sometimes a weak spot also and herbal teas may be found to be helpful here. There is also a tendency to build up tensions at the back of the neck (Atlas and Axis bones) and to retain mucus which causes catarrh and often makes Taureans heavy and rather slow. They have a strong constitution, however, and many remain superbly healthy.

They benefit from a natural diet and in any case need to moderate their love of rich food and good wine. Herbal medicine will usually prove to be effective for them and also the Bach flower remedies.

The tissue salt which they find difficult to assimilate and which they need to eliminate fluids is Sulphate of Soda (*Nat. Sulph.*). This is indicated when they are not feeling up to par or when they are feeling strained or worried.

For exercise they will enjoy walking, probably golf, swimming and dancing. They are usually excellent at both of the latter and these are extremely valuable exercises for them.

For relaxation, the pursuit of their artistic hobbies (provided that this is not their everyday job), music, gardening, fishing, and in general keeping in touch with nature is the way the Taurean recharges his batteries.

These people enjoy massage (this should be a stimulating one with the idea of breaking down the fatty tissue) and particularly aromatherapy.

As regards homoeopathic remedies, Taureans are often the 'Pulsatilla' type and among the other remedies they are likely to find useful are Calendula tincture for hay fever and Arnica for shock.

Among the herbs which may be useful to the Taurean are:

Bilberry which helps to counteract water retention.

Blackcurrant for throat infections and catarrh and also for the prevention and treatment of goitre.

Chicory is a valuable help to get rid of excess mucus.

Elderberry is useful for all dropsical conditions.

Horseradish and Hyssop are both valuable for catarrh, bronchitis and reducing mucus.

Sage is soothing for throat ulcers and may be used as a gargle.

Sunflower tea is recommended for bronchitis, laryngitis, coughs and colds.

All Taureans should take Kelp regularly as the iodine helps to prevent goitre. They should also grow Fenugreek for nutrition and as a help to control sore throats.

The Bach remedy most applicable to the Taurean is Vervain, but as I have already suggested, these people are likely to react well to all the Bach remedies and I would suggest that they purchase one of the books describing them (see Further Information) and then make a suitable selection to keep in the house.

Their attitude to illness tends to be pessimistic, and this together with their stubborness in obeying orders (if they think they know better) may mean that their illnesses tend to be prolonged. They belong to the class of people who will weather a great deal of trouble and remain patient and stable, but depression may overtake them very quickly if they become ill themselves. A negative attitude to health is common, and they are more inclined to put up with ill health than to seek actively for a remedy.

Psychologically, the Taurean has a great need to be 'earthed' – to feel solid ground under his feet. This makes him obstinate in his opinions and he finds it difficult to accept that other people have a right to think differently. His possessiveness also tends to deny that his loved ones are people in their own right rather than his possessions. Both of these attitudes can make it particularly difficult where his own children are concerned as the generation gap can be very wide indeed if he is not prepared to update his opinions. Normally, however, Taureans enjoy good relationships with their children and love their homes.

To become psychologically whole and to progress spiritually, the Taurean needs to recognise these two major defects and to become more tolerant and generous.

Gemini

The Sun is in the sign of Gemini (the twins) from about 21 May to 20 June. You would also be considered a Gemini type if the Moon or Mercury is in this sign, or, of course, if it is in the Ascendant.

The Geminian is an Air type, and is vitally concerned with all matters of communication. He is a pastmaster in the art of words, both in writing and speech, and his mentality is very quick and active.

As he is a 'mental' type, rather than a feeling or emotional type, the typical Geminian does not form deep and lasting relationships with others (though, of course, no birth chart is all Gemini). It would be true to say that he does not become attached to places either – or even to his own ideas. His is a world of movement, where opinions change rapidly as new information is acquired, and he is quite capable of playing devil's advocate if the fit takes him, being a skilled debater and extremely quick witted. He is also prone to self-deception as he can easily convince himself that his latest opinion is the one he has always held.

He hates being tied down and will run a mile from routine, drudgery or monotony. In fact, words beginning with 'mono' are not in his vocabulary, for Gemini is the sign of duality and he is often equally as competent with his hands as he is with his brain. He tends to undertake too many projects at once and it often calls for strict discipline to get any of them completed. If practicality and responsibility are not shown elsewhere in the birth chart, the true Geminian can be a typical 'Jack of all trades and master of none'. He tends to be restless and always feels that the grass is greener elsewhere.

Despite his disinclination to form close attachments, the Geminian, like all the Air signs, must have company. He needs people with whom to exchange ideas. His ideal life partner would be someone who shared his ideas and stimulated him mentally. He would not be possessive and would not tolerate this trait in others.

Gemini children can become depressed if their natural energy and eagerness is over-restricted, just as the older Geminian can suffer from psychosomatic illnesses caused by boredom. It is important, therefore, that their careers should be suitable to them and keep their lively minds interested. They dislike being tied to office hours and will tend to find their careers in situations where they are largely in charge of their own life and can work whatever hours suit them. Suitable careers are those of commercial salesman, newspaper reporter, freelance journalist, courier and similar situations where the hours are irregular but where they are engaged in movement or the exchange of ideas.

Air must move or it becomes stagnant and in the same way the Geminian will feel threatened and hemmed in by restrictive conditions.

The ruler of Gemini is Mercury which has to do with all methods of communication and, in particular, rules the nervous system, which of course carries communications from the brain to the rest of the body. The Geminian's quickness of mind and movement means that he is often very intelligent and adaptable but tends to undertake too much and to suffer from nervous exhaustion and nerve troubles generally. Above all, Geminians need to relax and this they find very difficult to do. Yoga is one of the best forms of relaxation for them as it quietens the mind and the exercises are slow and controlled. Geminians are just the type of people who would get too interested in the mechanics of Bio-feedback and so fail to achieve results with it.

On an emotional level, these people often appear rather cold-natured. They value the mind above the heart and tend to conceal their deeper feelings. Like all the Air signs, they can get very upset by quarrels and it is perhaps for this reason that they tend to remain rather aloof.

Gemini rules the hands, arms and shoulders, also the lungs and nervous system. This carries a tendency to bronchial and lung troubles, asthma and neuritis. Geminians who use their hands and shoulders all day in such jobs as typing often become prone to muscular troubles in that region. This condition can be much relieved by massage and suitable exercises.

Many Geminians enjoy fencing, which exercises these muscles and which calls for coordination of the hand and eye. They need quite a lot of outdoor exercise, enough to induce healthy exhaustion, so that both body and mind become relaxed. Mentally stimulating activities should be avoided at night, otherwise the Geminian will go short of the sleep which he so badly needs to make sure that his over-active mind gets a good period of rest. Eurythmy, which combines dance movement with control and meaning, may appeal to the Geminian. His greatest enemy is boredom which is one reason why he always wants to keep fully occupied. However, this can result in very little being actually completed as he tends to flit from one activity to another. Anything which makes for self-discipline in his life can only benefit him and the controlled movements of yoga and eurythmy are two good examples of this.

As regards healing techniques he is likely to react positively to reflexology, massage and aromatherapy, while chiropractic and osteopathy may help to overcome any shoulder pains.

Among the homoeopathic remedies which he may find useful are arnica for shocks, *Nux. Vom.* for nervous indigestion and nervous headaches and euphrasia tincture for hayfever. His tissue salt is Potassium Chloride (*Kali. Mur.*) which is a blood conditioner and prevents lung troubles.

His diet should be balanced and include as much vegetables and fruit as possible.

Among the herbs which the Geminian is likely to find useful are the following:

Bergamot which will help to induce relaxation and sleep.

Borage which is a good nerve tonic.

Garlic for the chest and lungs.

Horseradish which helps to relieve bronchial catarrh.

Lavender which is a nerve soother and is a herb of Gemini.

Nettle which is another good blood purifier.

Sunflower for all bronchial troubles.

Among the Bach flower remedies it is likely that Agrimony will be useful to some Geminians. You should read the description of this in the Bach flower remedies to decide whether it is for you.

The Geminian finds it difficult to find time to stop and listen to his inner self. As I have already said he prizes his knowledge above all and the head more than the heart. However his esoteric ruler is Venus and this gives a clue to what is necessary for him to progress on both psychological and spiritual lines. He needs to make close relationships and to express the emotions which he feels. The constant pursuit of *things* which leaves little time for *people* means that the Geminian often has many acquaintances but no close friends. Such superficial relationships may fail him and leave him lonely – a sad fate for such a gregarious person with a need to communicate. If this is to be avoided he needs to allocate some of his precious time to contemplation and to the cultivation of deeper relationships.

In the evolved Geminian we see the mental faculties being used to evaluate and judge objectively. He no longer reacts instinctively to a situation but can decide on the wisest course and always remains flexible in his attitude. His insatiable curiosity is now used to seek for the deeper meanings in life and like his opposing sign, Sagittarius, he can become 'The happy philosopher'.

Cancer

The Sun is in Cancer from about 21 June to 22 July, but you may also have many characteristics of this sign if you have Cancer in the Ascendant and especially if you have the Moon in Cancer.

The Moon is the ruler of this sign and in the same way that it affects the tides and rhythms of the Earth, so it indicates the fluctuations in mood of the Cancer subject. These people often get depressed (for no obvious reason) and then feel 'on top of the world' a few days later. Some of them are able to relate their moods very precisely to the phases of the Moon, so it is worth watching it for a few months to see whether you are one of these people. If you find that you are always at your best when the Moon is new, or full, and that your spirits fall just before the New Moon, or when it is waning, you may be able to regulate your life in some ways, so that you do not plan an outing at a time when you are not going to feel like it, for instance. It may also help you to know, if you are feeling low, that things will improve in a few days.

The correlation with the menstrual cycle is very obvious, but Cancerian men also experience these fluctuations of mood and energy.

Cancer is, above all, the maternal sign. Like all the other water signs, Cancerians are intuitive and emotional. While they are caring people and fiercely protective of their offspring (be it a child, a project or just an idea) they are also tenacious and find it difficult to let their children lead their own lives when they grow up. They are *the* worriers of the zodiac – over big things and small, and often seem even more worried if they have nothing to worry about.

Being emotional, they are much more easily hurt than they show, and they also tend to dwell in the past so that past hurts are brooded over. This is true of all the Water signs, but particularly of Cancerians. It is, of course, a sheer waste of his energy and hurts no one but himself.

Psychologically, Cancerians have a great need to make a nest – they must have a base and someone to look after otherwise they feel that their life is not worthwhile.

In true maternal fashion, they are usually good homemakers and great cooks. They encourage their family to 'eat it all up – it will do you good', and this is fatal to the typical Cancerian who usually has a battle with weight like the other Water signs. This is partly a tendency to retain fluid, as well as a propensity to over-indulge in home-made dishes. These can easily upset a digestive system that is already under attack by the Cancerian's habit of worrying. They should never take a meal when they are upset about anything.

As well as being protective people themselves, Cancerians also need to feel protected and appreciated. They are over-quick to imagine slights and rejections, often where it is not intended, and they can become self-pitying and bitter. They need a warm, demonstrative family to keep them happy.

They are tenacious and loyal and can be very strong for other people, especially family members, if they are in difficulties. Then their best qualities will be shown, not only in caring for the afflicted person but in taking charge of the situation and seeing it through. They have a deep and intuitive compassion for others and can share their feelings.

Conversely, with their own difficulties they quickly get depressed and can be sunk in gloom within a very short space of time. Like the Pisceans, their depressions can often spring from nameless fears – anticipating disasters which may never happen.

They need to feel secure and will work hard to provide a

sound financial base. They are not at all extravagant with money, but will always pay for quality.

All of the careers which involve looking after people or things will appeal to the Cancerian. Cooking and nursing both attract them and so do things connected with the past so that they are often found as antique dealers, caretakers, historians and researchers. Many of them are also attracted to artistic pursuits.

Their feeling for the past and their instinct to preserve things can sometimes mean that they live in a world of memories, surrounded by the nick nacks of a bygone age. They like collecting things and sometimes what they collect is just clutter. They value everything which is old and tend to be suspicious of the new.

In the same way, their minds may be cluttered by past failures and mistakes (or real or imagined slights from others). The inability to forget is often what stops the Cancerian from progressing. They remember life's lessons but they also remember and brood over things better forgotten.

When they are cheerful they have a strong sense of humour and usually have excellent health at such times. They attract illness to them when they become gloomy and pessimistic, thus setting up a vicious circle.

The parts of the body ruled by Cancer are the breasts, stomach and alimentary canal. Worry and tension affect them by causing nervous indigestion, ulcers, gastritis, constipation and other stomach troubles.

They need regular exercise to 'fight the flab' and dancing often appeals to them. They also enjoy team games but do not like dangerous sport as their sense of self-preservation is very strong.

Most Cancerians need massage to help eliminate fluid and to break down fatty tissue. They will also respond well to healing, Nature Cure and to the Bach flower remedies.

Natural foods, especially the fibrous material such as bran and whole fruits (including the skins of apples and pears, etc.)

are valuable to them as aids to elimination. As they are creative cooks, they will usually enjoy experimenting with whole foods and evolving their own recipes, to the great benefit of their families as well as themselves.

The worrying nature and the sense of self-preservation can turn the Cancerian into a hypochondriac. This is dangerous, for there is no doubt that people can will themselves into a state of ill health simply by dwelling on it. The only way to combat this tendency is to be too busy to worry about minor ailments – it is amazing how many of them just disappear if they are ignored. This is not to suggest that chronic conditions should be disregarded, but there is no fear of that happening with a Cancerian. In the same way, it is easy for the Cancerian parent to turn a child into a hypochondriac by continually fussing about every little ailment. Children are more resiliant than most Cancerian parents think, but they will not withstand a whole childhood of being taught to worry about themselves without carrying it over into adult life.

Cancerians can usually relax well, when they allow themselves to do so, and only need to be 'taken out of themselves'. Most of them will enjoy Eurythmy and creative activities.

Among the homoeopathic remedies which should prove useful, the Cancerian should keep *Nux. Vom.* 6 for stomach upsets and nervous indigestion. These people are likely to be Pulsatilla types, and if this seems applicable, Pulsatilla 30 is a good standby.

The tissue salt for Cancerians is Fluoride of Lime (*Calc. Fluor.*), which helps the elasticity of the tissues and so prevents varicose veins and prolapses.

Among the herbs which the Cancerian may find useful are the following:

Arrowroot which calms the stomach.

Balm which also helps to do this and is invaluable for infertility and irregular menses.

Bilberry which helps to counteract water retention.

Caraway is useful for nursing mothers.

Cloves help to clear stomach gases.

Fenugreek soothes inflammation of the stomach.

Fennel is good for nursing mothers and will relieve flatulence.

Lovage is a cure for dysmenorrhea and for stomach disorders generally.

Mustard helps to prevent indigestion.

There are two Bach flower remedies which may be applicable to Cancerians. These are Chicory and Cerato (see the descriptions under the Flower Remedies).

The natural characteristic of the motherly Cancer type is to carry the children's burdens. Most of their worrying is for other people rather than for themselves and consists largely of a dread of what may happen. It may help them to realise that all worrying is a rehearsal for what may never occur and, like the brooding on the past, it is a waste of time and energy (and often of health). Both psychologically and spiritually, the Cancerian needs to cultivate a sense of detachment – to be more concerned about themselves and less about others (whose lives they cannot affect, no matter how much they may wish to bear other people's troubles). Their spiritual path is to find the peace within.

Leo

The Sun is in this sign from about 23 July to 22 August. People with Leo Ascendants or Moon in Leo will also show some of the characteristics of the type, but the Sun is the ruler of this sign, so it is the people born between these dates who are likely to show the Leo temperament most strongly.

Like their ruler, most Leos have a sunny, optimistic disposition. Generous and good-natured, they never lack friends, but they expect to be the recognised leader. Just as the Sun in any birth chart expresses the personality, so Leo's great need is to express himself fully and to do this he must be 'somebody' or he feels he is nobody. He is a born organiser (or boss!) and often finds himself elected to these positions as other people recognise his qualities of leadership.

Like another of the Fire signs, Aries, he is dynamic and a go-getter but he also has the practicality that Aries lacks. This means that he often ends up in positions of power in the business world where he may over-drive and over-exhaust himself. Leo rules the heart, spine, gall bladder and cardiac system and this type of life makes him a number one target for a coronary attack. However, it is easy to avoid, if Leos are aware of the problem and make an effort to see that they do not get into this situation. As a typical Fire sign, he is courageous and optimistic and tends to overestimate the amount which he can achieve. He is also too proud to ask for help from other people very often and for this reason (and because he wants to show others that he can do it all) he gets into the sort of situation where the pressure is more than he can take.

He is a lover of life and he wants to lead it to the full. However, he will be quite happy to let other people see to the small details which he feels are too trivial for him to bother with. He can allow his dignity or sense of self-importance to get out of hand, and can then inhibit the self-expression which is so necessary a part of his character. In the normal way, the Fire signs are unimaginative and tend to act out their emotions so that they do not become vulnerable to mental or emotional troubles. But a Leo who 'bottles up' his feelings for fear he should appear undignified may pay for this by getting into a position where he discovers it is lonely at the top. Since he is a consummate actor, it is unlikely that anyone will sense the loneliness behind the mask of bonhomie which Leo normally radiates. Because of his courage he often seems to be more confident when he is most vulnerable. I knew a 'Lioness' who bought a fur coat on the day that she lost her job and swaggered off as though she owned the world – a typical example of her sign.

Leo is the sign of the intensely unique personality. One who has realised himself fully – in Jung's words, one who has achieved individuation. He must create and expand, turning his potential into actuality. To this task he brings great enthusiasm, expressing the joy of living in no uncertain terms. But he needs, in return, the adulation of those about him – a receptive and applauding audience for his one man show.

If this is lacking, he may engage in the practice known in some types of psychology as 'negative stroking' – putting other people down in order to feel better about himself. An angry lion is often a sad one, and a little genuine praise and loving is all that is needed to bring back the old, confident, optimistic Leo.

The arrogant pride which he sometimes displays is nothing more than a cover-up for an inferiority complex – a most unlikely thing for a Leo to have, but one which can be engendered by an over-repressive childhood. The parents of a Leo child have no small task in striking the balance between allowing their offspring to be blatantly bossy and dampening his enthusiasm by continually cutting him down to size.

The Leo type can become domineering and rather overbearing, but if this is avoided there is no doubt that they are probably the kindest sign of the zodiac. They are particularly good with children, and because they like other people to be as happy and optimistic as they are, they enjoy the sort of jobs in which they are giving pleasure to the public. One finds them as actors, entertainers of all kind, fashion designers, jewellers, etc. However, they may also be found in the realm of big business and politics where they will undoubtedly take a leading role.

Apart from the ailments of the heart, Leos are also prone to feverish conditions, back pains, spinal disorders, rheumatic fever and arterio-sclerosis.

They would be well advised to learn the Alexander technique to avoid the back and spinal troubles, and they would probably react positively to chiropractic and herbal treatment.

They need exercise which will give the heart a good work out and would probably enjoy gymnastics and competitive sport where they can excel.

If their work is exhausting however they should not go into competition and would be better as part of a team. They will find relaxation in drama and in creative activities. Anything which allows them to act out feelings will be especially therapeutic, particularly if their job is frustrating or does not give them scope for self-expression.

Among the homoeopathic remedies which Leo may find useful are the following:

Urtica Urens (tincture or tablets 6) for relief from nettlerash, which is a kind of fever, and for burns and scalds.

Nux. Vom. 30 when feeling under strain.

Aconitum 30 for palpitations caused by tension.

Phosphate of Magnesium (Mag. Phos.) is the Leo tissue salt, which maintains vigour and the fluidity of the blood. Among the herbs useful to Leo are the following:

Angelica which cures heartburn and is a good general tonic.

Borage is a blood purifier and cools fevers.

Dandelion as its name implies, is a herb of Leo which is a tonic and blood purifier.

Hyssop helps to regulate blood-pressure.

Mustard will alleviate back pains.

Nettle should be used as a spring tonic. It improves circulation and is an excellent blood purifier.

Rosemary is a heart tonic which reduces blood-pressure.

Witch Hazel stems bleeding and is antiseptic.

The Leo diet should contain wholewheat, green vegetables and some eggs (not more than two or three a week).

Psychologically, the Leo native needs to learn to appreciate the unique qualities of other people. If he can do this, he will not fall into the trap of considering himself superior to them – a path which can lead to loneliness and deprive him of the company which his gregarious nature needs so much.

He must avoid taking himself too seriously and standing on his dignity with others. If he allows his warm hearted and generous nature full expression he will never be short of friends.

He must express himself if he is to be psychologically whole. If his work does not allow him to do this, he should change it if possible. If not, he should make sure that his sport or hobby will fill this need.

Virgo

The Sun is in the sign of Virgo from about 23 August to 22 September, but you will also be considered a Virgo type if this sign is rising (in the Ascendant) at the time of your birth, or if the Moon or Mercury are in Virgo.

This is an Earth sign, ruled by Mercury and the Virgoan has the practical and responsible nature of the Earth types together with the rather nervy Mercurial pattern, which in Gemini showed itself in always being on the move, but in Virgo is seen in a general fussiness.

Virgo brings orderliness to the Mercury traits in true practical (Earth) fashion. He really cannot put up with muddle or delay. Though he will patiently sort out the smallest detail, he can get very impatient at delay and always tends to look for someone to blame if things don't go his way.

Nothing is ever quite right for the Virgo type, especially if someone else has done the work, and great effort is put into doing everything as precisely as possible. The Virgoan sets very high standards both for himself and for others and being a perfectionist is never satisfied with what is achieved. He is a hard worker (the best in the zodiac) but depletes his energies by the vast amount of effort put into each tiny detail and he often needs to work hard to get as much done as his more relaxed colleague.

In many ways, Virgo, the next sign in the zodiac to Leo, is the exact opposite. Where Leo has the wide vision and the capacity to organise on a grand scale, Virgo is concerned with all the small details. He brings Leo's grandiose plans down to earth, in effect. The Mercury rulership of Virgo gives the Virgoan an interest in and respect for hard facts. He values knowledge for its own sake. Like the other Earth sign of Taurus, the instinct for value is strong, but here it is related to thought and judgement rather than to possessions. The brain is scientific, mistrusting anything which cannot be proved logically or experienced physically.

It follows that he is happiest in a career which calls for precision – for instance, as a draughtsman, in all kinds of checking work, factory inspectors, in research as chemist or scientist and so on. Being a child of Mercury, he is also interested in communication and will make a good teacher or writer, book reviewer or drama critic. Office work, with its rigid routines and set hours is enjoyed by the practical Virgoan and the women of this sign are often found as secretaries and personal assistants. In typing jobs, like the Geminian, they are inclined to suffer from strain in the shoulders and upper arms.

They are not really suited to being in charge of staff, as they find it difficult to delegate work, being convinced that no-one will do it as well and as thoroughly as themselves. They can be highly critical and hard taskmasters. They seem to have abundant energy for work and often they do not appreciate that other people are not so lucky and are not just being lazy.

They tend to take on more work than they can comfortably do – and then do it.

This attitude can spill over into the private life and it is perhaps for this reason that the Virgoan is often a batchelor or spinster and sometimes a rather lonely person, despite his deep desire to be of service to others.

The sign of Virgo is also much associated with health, work and service. Virgoans tend to be interested in health and take jobs in connection with this. As they also like to feel that they are giving a service to others they are very often found in jobs such as that of social worker.

One of the reasons for his great interest in health is that the Virgoan cannot bear to have anything at all wrong with him. Someone with a blemish on his skin will not leave it alone to get better – it niggles at him and his mind will concentrate on it to the exclusion of all else.

Virgoans find it extremely difficult to relax as they are always conscious of some little detail which needs to be fixed, some more work which they feel they must do. They are not happy in jobs where their work is likely to accumulate at times, so that they cannot get a day's work finished in a day. This situation worries them very much and it is in their own interest to make sure that they do not get into such a position.

Their great need is to learn to accept something less than their very high standard, which is often not possible to achieve. Both for themselves and for other people they are often much too hard in the standards which they set. This can lead to all sorts of tensions which may result in many types of ill health.

The part of the body associated with Virgo is the intestines and the abdomen as well as the hands. They are liable to suffer from digestive troubles, diarrhoea, peritonitis, colitis and hernia. All of these are troubles which can be avoided by the right type of life style for the Virgoan.

Natural foods are especially indicated in the diet of the sign which represents the corn goddess, and in particular, of course, whole grains. Virgoans can be extremely fussy about their food almost to a point of crankiness, but if this can be avoided there is no doubt that they are sensible in taking particular care that they eat unrefined foods and like a natural, healthy diet.

Among the homoeopathic remedies, the Virgoan should keep *Nux. Vom.* 6 available for nervous indigestion and nervous headaches caused by anxiety and Arsenicum 30 as a standby for times when they are particularly tense and under pressure of work. Homoeopathy is specially indicated for Virgoans, as they like the precision necessary to find exactly the right remedy.

The tissue salt for Virgo is Potassium Sulphate *(Kali. Sulph.)* which prevents the clogging of pores and rebuilds the nerve cells.

Several herbs are helpful and, being an Earth sign, the Virgoan is likely to react well to these. They are as follows:

Angelica which stimulates the digestive tract.

Balm which soothes it and is good for nervous troubles.

Borage which has a similar reaction.

Caraway which stimulates the digestion and is also very versatile (see Herbs) and this should always be available to the Virgoan.

Cloves are soothing and antiseptic and will help to clear stomach gases.

Dill is especially a herb of Virgo and is noted for cleansing the digestive tract.

Fennel is also a herb of Virgo and it will relieve flatulence and is a good disinfectant.

Fenugreek will be found useful for inflammation of the intestines.

Sage is also a digestive.

There are several Bach flower remedies which may be appropriate for the Virgoan and the native is advised to choose between them after having read the descriptions under that heading. These are Centaury, Impatiens and Vervain.

As regards exercise, the Virgoan should be concerned to preserve movement. Brisk walking or anything fairly strenuous which gives good exercise to all the muscles concerned with movement will be beneficial.

In order to help him to relax and also to overcome psychological difficulties, the Virgoan would benefit from meditation. Although his standards are so high and he easily finds fault with people, he is, nevertheless, a basically shy and retiring person and tends to lack self-confidence. This, of course, is partly because of the very high standards which he sets himself and which can mean that he is foredoomed to failure. The type of meditation that he needs, would help him to discover, appreciate and truly become what he really is. He tends to be hedged about with 'oughts and shoulds' and he needs to accept and forgive both himself and others and love them as they are 'warts and all'. His service to others tends to be judgemental and is given only to those whom he considers worthy. Psychological and spiritual progress for this sign depends on his coming to terms with his own humanity and that of others, and ceasing to expect the impossible.

Libra

The Sun is in this sign from about 23 September to 22 October, but you may also be a Libra type if you have the Moon or Venus in this sign or if it is on the Ascendant. It is an Air sign and it is ruled by the planet Venus the goddess of love and of beauty. This makes the Libran a communicative person, much concerned with personal relationships.

His urge is to find the life-partner and this needs to be someone with whom he can communicate. A marriage that does not satisfy him mentally, as well as physically, will not be at all satisfactory to the Libran.

Traditionally, he is a charming, easy-going person, who likes life to be pleasant. Like the Taurean (the other sign ruled by Venus) he also appreciates all the luxuries of life. He has a reputation for laziness, but, although he is quite willing to let other people do things for him, he is very capable of asserting himself in his own interests.

The sign for Libra is that of the Scales (or balance) and he uses his mind to 'weigh up' arguments. So good is he at seeing both sides of a question that he frequently finds it difficult to reach a conclusion. This dithering can affect his nervous system (as with most Air subjects) and he can take refuge in psychosomatic illnesses in order to avoid reaching decisions in matters which are crucial.

His obsession with justice is such that anything unfair distresses him enormously. He likes to right wrongs whenever possible and is often cast in the role of a peacemaker. Consequently, he does well in diplomatic circles, or in jobs where he acts as agent for two groups of people, such as an auctioneer, receptionist or solicitor. He may also be happy in any career where he is handling beautiful objects or in the artistic trades, such as hairdresser. It is most important that he should not be forced to work in surroundings or with people who are not congenial to him. He cannot cope with this situation and may quickly become ill in such circumstances.

The Libran has a very sensitive nature, and perhaps more than any other zodiacal type, can easily become physically ill (though the reason is certainly psychological) through pressures which other people would take in their stride. He is especially resentful of anything which appears to be unfair and which affects him personally and can brood upon his wrongs (real or imagined) long after the perpetrators of the injustice have forgotten about them. For this reason, he often makes enemies, while feeling that the other person must be wrong, since he himself would rather make friends.

Since he is intelligent and shrewd, he often makes a good business man and does well at running his own business either by himself or with a partner. This is in many ways the ideal solution to his problem of injustice since he is not in a position where superiors can put him down or make him feel small. However, this is not always possible and the Libran really needs to cultivate a more philosophical attitude and to realise that he is not the only one who is affected by the fact that life is not always fair.

The parts of the body said to be ruled by Libra are the kidneys, the renal system and lumbar area, and consequently Librans are liable to suffer from lumbago, kidney and bladder troubles, ulcers, diabetes and ovarian cysts. However, as they are good at balancing their activities and their diet they are usually one of the healthiest signs of the zodiac. They are likely to respond well to radionics treatment and to the Bach flower remedies.

Like all the Air signs, they must move and they need exercise every day. They will probably be interested in all types of team games and, like the Geminians, they are often attracted to fencing which is an exercise in balance. For relaxation, any artistic pursuit (provided it is not their full time job) is likely to attract them and they will also respond well to aromatherapy.

As regards diet, the main thing is that they should watch the balance between the acids and the alkalis. For this reason the tissue salt for Librans is Sodium Phosphate (*Nat. Phos.*) which does this and thereby helps to prevent acidity. The tissue salt of Capricorn which is *Calc. Phos.* can help to prevent kidney troubles. The planet Saturn is said to be exalted in Libra and this is one of the applications which can be useful to the Libran.

As regards the homoeopathic remedies, the one which is particularly indicated for Libra is Chamomilla 30, which is especially suited for restless and indecisive natures.

Several herbs are useful to the Libran and these include:

Bilberry which is diuretic and promotes kidney action.

Borage activates the kidneys and cures jaundice.

Dandelion has many advantages for the Libran (see Herbs).

Parsley is a recognised kidney tonic.

Horseradish is a Libran herb which helps all kidney troubles.

Thyme which is cleansing and antiseptic, helps to relieve headaches caused by kidney disorders and is especially a herb of Libra. This should be grown by all Librans and should never be picked wild as it accumulates lead and can be affected by car fumes.

As regards the Bach flower remedies, there are four which may apply to the Libran and the description of these should be read and the appropriate one selected. These are Agrimony, Cerato, Scleranthus and Mimulus.

Psychologically, the Libran needs to be aware that he is inclined to carry a sense of grievance to unjustifiable lengths. If he is not to become the type of disgruntled person whom other people don't want to know he needs to come to terms with this and to cultivate the type of self-sufficiency which accepts that his life is largely in his own hands and that other people cannot do things to him unless he allows them to. For this reason, I would suggest that some of the encounter groups may be helpful. If you are a typical Libran, you are likely to be horrified by this suggestion but I would remind you that the therapy to which we are most resistant is the one which we usually need most.

Like the Virgoan, the Libran can be very critical of other people and for this reason he often tends to cling to the one partner and not make the close friendships which he would desire. From a spiritual point of view, he needs to be more out-reaching to other people and to show a generosity of spirit in acknowledging that he too has his faults.

If I seem to have been rather hard on the Libran, who is universally acknowledged as being a gentle, peace-loving, friendly person, this is because in a book such as this I need to emphasise the difficulties in the psychological make up which can cause illness and not because I do not appreciate the fine characteristics of all of the zodiacal signs. Every sign has its strengths and its weaknesses but, unfortunately, it is the weaknesses usually that cause illness or disease.

Scorpio

The Sun is in this sign from about 23 October to 21 November, but you may also be considered a Scorpio type if this sign is in the Ascendant (rising at the time of birth) or if it contains the Moon or Pluto.

Before we knew of the outer planets, Scorpio was thought to be ruled by Mars, and you will see that it does share some characteristics of Aries, of which Mars is the ruler. There is the same passion and driving force in the nature of the Scorpion. However, this is a Water sign, and, so there is also an emotional and intuitive quality which was lacking in Aries.

The Pluto rulership is also confirmed, I believe, by a 'refining and regenerating' influence which is so often part of the Scorpion's life pattern. The characteristic of Pluto seems to be to exteriorise things (some of which we would rather keep hidden) and so to enable us to deal with them, often by discarding attitudes which are no longer helpful if we are to obtain our goals. So we often find the Scorpio native making complete changes in his way of life – usually to the surprise of his friends, as he will have given no previous indication of this. Like his ruler, Pluto (the god of the underworld in mythology), he works in darkness – which is to say, in secret, until the time is right to reveal his plans. Because he is also an intuitive (Water) type, a great deal goes on under the surface, and as he is also sensitive to the opinions of others, he has every reason to be secretive. The phrase 'still waters run deep' might have been written of the Scorpion. In the same way, he will respect the confidences of other people.

The great intensity of his feelings is best expressed in the way he puts his whole heart into everything – work, play, love, hobbies – he feels passionately about them all. Obviously, such a nature can cause havoc and even erupt into violence if it takes that road, and for this reason the old astrologers often labelled Scorpios as the bad boys of the zodiac. Nothing could be further from the truth for the majority of them, as many feel passionately about their fellow man and will do all in their power (which is to say, a great deal) to help others.

Being a Water sign, they are involved with other people and empathise with them. They are easily hurt by others and, in particular, tend to be too concerned about other people's opinions of them. This often stops them from making those changes in their lives which they instinctively know are right for them (even though such changing might make no sense at all to other people). This is not a thing of the mind, or of judgement, but a deeply felt psychological need. This attitude to others will also explain the traditional secretiveness of this sign.

However, like another Water sign, Cancer, he hides his hurts and on the surface Scorpio appears calm and controlled. His is, in fact, a very strong personality. He has a great deal of personal power and although his is a Water sign, relating to the emotions, he has a great strength of purpose, courage and perseverance. His tremendous will can be used to control others, and if he chooses to use it in this way, he will accept personal responsibility for his actions.

He finds it difficult to compromise as his attitude is never ambivalent. He either loves or hates – unless, of course, he is icily indifferent. His sign is Fixed Water which can only be ice, and this can be manifested by the Scorpion at times.

Like his opposite sign, Taurus, the Scorpio native has a sensual nature and can quickly get jealous and possessive. The sting in the Scorpion's tail can also be shown in a sarcastic, biting wit, with the intention of 'scoring off' other people. He can also be quite ruthless if he feels he has been exploited or if others are thwarting his plans. The single-mindedness of Mars as shown in Aries, also has its counterpart in Scorpio and he will not be satisfied with casual affairs. His emotions must be deeply engaged and then he will be faithful to his chosen partner.

The evolved Scorpion is aware of both his power and his responsibility. He has learnt how to enjoy without wanting to possess. He understands when to stop and let go and can put behind him – and forget about – past experiences which are no longer relevant to his growth. He has also learned to respect the rights of others.

He is shrewd and logical, yet he definitely has a sure instinct for summing up people and knows who he can trust. To them he will be a wise counsellor and a loyal friend.

Because of his intensity, the Scorpion needs rest and in particular *mental* relaxation, if he is to remain healthy. Although he meets difficulties with courage, he can get very depressed and this is partly self-induced since he can be unreasonably suspicious.

Scorpio rules the throat and nasal passages (Taurus polarity), the pelvis, sexual organs, generative system, bladder, rectum and prostate gland, and this sign tends to suffer from troubles in these areas of the body, also from epilepsy, hernia, painful menstruation and constipation. They tend to catch infections easily, especially those of the nose and throat.

The native will respond to healing and acupressure. Biofeedback may help him to relax his mind but he also needs to find a creative hobby for this purpose. Relaxing massage is usually enjoyed by Scorpios.

Any exercise which he enjoys will be beneficial, and he will probably like competitive sport where he can set his own goals. Walking is most beneficial to him, especially to prevent constipation.

Again, like Taurus, he benefits from contact with nature. His diet should not contain highly spiced foods or stimulants. Leeks, onions, kale, prunes and coconut are all valuable to him.

Among the homoeopathic remedies, he will probably find *Nux. Vom.* 6 useful for haemorrhoids, and constipation, and he should take Pulsatilla 30, when appropriate.

Tissue salts are especially indicated for the Scorpion, and in particular Sulphate of Lime (*Calc. Sulph.*). A full description of these are given elsewhere in this book.

Among the Bach flower remedies, Impatiens may be appropriate at times. There are many herbs to help Scorpio's illnesses:

Basil is useful as a stimulant and for the healing of wounds.

Ginseng is also a stimulant and is particularly considered to be 'ruled' by Scorpio.

Bilberry helps to overcome water retention.

Elderberry has the same effect and also soothes burns and scalds.

Chicory is a good laxative.

Witch Hazel is helpful for haemorrhoids.

Sage will staunch bleeding and is also good for throat ailments.

Olive is also a good laxative.

Lovage is a good general tonic which will benefit Scorpios.

Kelp should also be taken by them to provide iron and to reduce the chance of goitres.

Psychologically, the Scorpio native has to battle with his own intensity and needs to seek peace within himself. He has to learn to be unconcerned about the opinions of others, as long as he knows where he is going. He needs to be less secretive with others if they are upsetting him, as he can 'bottle up' these feelings until the inner tension suddenly erupts and relationships are destroyed.

Psychosomatic illnesses can come from repressing the urge to do what the Scorpio instinctively knows is right for him. Like all the Water signs, he needs to cultivate a sense of detachment from others, and become aware of his own unique values.

He is interested in obscure and occult matters and has a great urge to get to the bottom of life's mysteries so he is often attracted to the study of psychology and if he can be detached enough to apply this knowledge to himself, he will be able to cultivate the right climate for his own growth and health.

Sagittarius

The Sun is in this sign from about 22 November to 21 December approximately. You would also share some of the Sagittarian characteristics if this sign was rising at the time of your birth or if the Moon or Jupiter was in Sagittarius then.

This is a Fire sign, ruled by Jupiter, so the native is outgoing and optimistic. Sagittarians show the expansiveness of Jupiter in their relaxed attitude, their wide-ranging interests and their broad tolerance towards others. They are on friendly terms with most of mankind, and many of them work in other countries or travel to other countries in the course of their work. So one gets the picture of the free-ranging individual whose life is firmly in his own hands and who pleases himself in what he does, and is usually contented – a happy-go-lucky fellow.

This attitude makes the Sagittarian less 'fiery' than the other Fire signs – Aries and Leo – but he does share their self-sufficient attitude. He cannot bear to be fenced in and he expects other people to respect his need for freedom, just as he respects theirs. He will quickly dodge any attempt to coerce him. Like the Geminian (his opposite sign) he is best in a job which he can run himself, without too many rigid restrictions. He does, however, need disciplines, or he can be over-expansive to the extent that his ideas may be too grandiose, and incapable of realisation. Time can cease to matter to him to such an extent that appointments are not kept and so on. People find it difficult to tie him down to any firm commitments, so that he may get the reputation of being unreliable.

However, if he can avoid falling into the trap of over-expansiveness, his Fire attributes give him plenty of vitality and a great urge to explore, both physically and mentally. His greatest enemy is boredom and he needs the stimulation of a challenge. His sign, Sagittarius means 'the Archer' and he is constantly aiming at something. He needs to cultivate practicality. Just as fire needs to move in order to burn brightly, but needs to be kept in bounds if it is not to become dangerous, so the Fire sign natives need the utmost freedom compatible with the demands of everyday living.

Within the marriage bond, the Sagittarian needs a partner who will appreciate this and not make him feel 'fenced in'. He also needs someone who can meet him on a mental level. He has interests in a wide number of subjects (often in a rather superficial way) but he is capable of deep study and can become completely absorbed in anything which really appeals to him.

He is a philosopher and knows better than to take life too seriously, so he does not usually suffer from psychosomatic illnesses (all the Fire signs are fairly free from these). The exception is when he really feels trapped by conditions about which he can do nothing. Illness is then a way of 'opting out'. This does not often happen, as Sagittarians can usually see these conditions coming a mile away and take evasive action at the first hint of danger.

Basically, the Sagittarian is a trusting person – not merely optimistic, but feeling in his bones 'God's in His heaven, all's right with the world.' Carried to extremes this attitude can result in the playboy type who expects everything to come his way without any effort on his part.

Jupiter is reputed to be the planet of good fortune and it is true that the Sagittarian often seems to have a happy life without a great deal of misfortune. How far his own optimistic nature contributes to this is impossible to say. Certainly we know that much sickness is caused by tension and worry and both of these give rise to psychological problems which in turn cause other misfortunes, so it seems likely that the Sagittarian's own relaxed attitude contributes to his well-being.

Like his opposite sign Gemini, he dislikes being tied down to routine conditions. Suitable careers for him can be found in professions in which his wide ranging intellect can be used. These are teacher, lawyer, priest, philosopher, and writer. He is also happy with outdoor work especially if it is connected with animals, and in particular horses, and in all forms of sport and exploration (including space-travel).

When he suffers from tiredness, it is usually mental and is often caused by boredom. As long as he is engrossed by something, the Sagittarian is rarely conscious of mental (or physical) fatigue. Such vitality must have outlets, and for many natives of this sign this is found in sport of all types – almost anything active appeals to them and with their 'hail-fellow-well-met' attitude to life, they enjoy playing in a team. Rugby football with its strong social side often appeals to them. They can get completely obsessive about their particular sport and this is a great pity since it not only bores other people, but also limits the native whose true nature is to be extremely versatile.

The parts of the body ruled by Sagittarius are the lower back, hips, thighs, liver and hepatic system. Jupiter's children can over-indulge their bodies and become 'liverish' and they need to limit their intake of rich foods.

They tend to suffer from accidents to the hips and legs, sciatica, enteric fever and respiratory troubles, as well as impairment of the liver function.

Sagittarians respond well to brisk massage, and deep remedial massage for muscle strains, but they have a wide tolerance of healing methods and are able to accept most types of treatment.

They must have outdoor exercise and, apart from all the sports, walking and riding are typically Sagittarian pursuits as are all activities which exercise the hips and thighs. They need to get into the open air and should not pursue sports which are only played indoors to the exclusion of the others.

For relaxation, massage is also a good way to 'wind down' so a brisk massage followed by a relaxing one would be excellent therapy for the Sagittarian. Meditation may also appeal since the Jupiterian is also a philosopher and often has an urge to look deeper into this subject.

In his diet, the Sagittarian needs to avoid rich foods and will benefit by ensuring that his meals contain green vegetables, liver, bran and oats.

Among the homoeopathic remedies he should keep *Nux. Vom.* 6 for liver upsets, *Rhus. Tox.* 6 for strained muscles, and *Hepar. Sulph.* 6 to assist boils to burst. The tissue salt, silica also helps to prevent, and to get rid of, styes and boils.

Herbs which should be useful to the Sagittarian are as follows:

Bay to stimulate the appetite and dissolve obstructions in the liver and spleen.

Borage is good for jaundice, and activates the digestive system.

Chicory is good for all liver conditions and is a herb of Jupiter.

Dandelion is a useful general tonic as well as helping the liver and kidneys.

Hyssop is a great cleanser and helps jaundice. It also relieves bruising.

Sage will staunch bleeding and helps the digestive system.

Thyme is cleansing and antiseptic. It is a good liver tonic and digestive.

Rosemary is also a good liver tonic and reduces blood pressure.

Fenugreek is valuable in the diet for nutritional purposes.

Lovage is carminative and reduces fevers.

Psychologically, the Sagittarian has few problems. His relaxed attitude to life keeps him largely free of the psychosomatic illnesses, but he needs to discipline himself to ensure that his expansive nature does not become over-expansive so that nothing is ever accomplished. He also needs to accept closer ties with others and to feel free *within* the restrictions of normal living. His tolerance for others is often because they do not matter very much to him, and this attitude can leave him lonely if all his relationships are on a superficial basis.

Capricorn

The Sun is in this sign from about 22 December to 20 January, but if Saturn or the Moon are in Capricorn, or if it is rising at the time of birth, the native will share some of the Capricorn characteristics.

This is an Earth sign ruled by Saturn, the planet of responsibility and practicality. Since all the Earth signs are like this Capricornians have a 'double dose' and are very reliable and firm (often to the point of obstinacy). Like all Earth signs, they have a great need for security and need a stable job.

They are always willing to help others in practical ways, but like their opposite sign of Cancer, they worry and easily become tense.

Capricornians are usually ambitious people, but they are also very patient and are willing to work and wait for results.

People tend to underrate them because they are often rather slow and plodding, but the one characteristic that beats all opposition is that they never give up. Even more than the Cancerian, they are the most tenacious and persevering of the zodiacal signs. They often achieve positions of power even though the results of their hard work may come rather late in life. Their ambition is for power, rather than for glory and they do not seek the limelight.

Like the Cancerians, they appreciate a happy home life, seeing themselves as the provider and father of the family and taking their duties and responsibilities seriously. They have a dry sense of humour and are by no means lacking a sense of fun. After all, the Roman Saturnalia was a great festival, celebrating the lengthening days as the year turned from Winter to Spring.

The Capricornian mother, like the Cancerian, can be guilty of 'smother-love' and tends to be over-fussy, though always generous and helpful.

The major cause of illness for the Capricornian is that he tends to 'bottle-up' emotions – in fact, he often gives the impression of not having any. His innate sense of dignity and popriety inhibits him from expressing his feelings. If, in addition, he has had the type of parents who have brought him up to 'keep a stiff upper lip' and to believe that 'big boys don't cry', they have laid the foundations for psychomatic illnesses, which may manifest in later life in nervous breakdowns or in diseases which restrict movement. It is, therefore, most important that Capricornians should learn to release tensions. It is also important that parents should realise what damage they can do to children by this rigid upbringing.

Most Capricornians have a built-in sense of timing. This is often rather slower than for most people, and many an Arian mother has battled with a Capricornian child, taking his time to get ready for school. However, they do get there in their own good time, and rather like the tortoise and the hare, they achieve their goals when others have exhausted themselves and fallen out of the race. For this reason, they do not suffer from the feverish conditions which attack the more energetic types, but they can sometimes neglect their own health. Capricornians are durable types, however, and most of them live to a ripe old age.

The Saturn influence often gives 'an old head on young shoulders' and many Capricornian children get on better with older people than with their own contemporaries. The best time of life for them is often when they are mature. By that time they have usually achieved their aims and they settle down into a contented later life.

Practical routine work, which provides security, will suit the Capricornian, but it needs to have prospects for promotion to the top rank. Careers in government, the Armed Forces and politics will appeal. Capricornians are also found in teaching, osteopathy, dentistry, science, engineering and building. They make good administrators of all types.

They can be over-conscientious and rather dogmatic. Their attitude can be rather inflexible and rigidity of mind is often found in a rigid body. If they wish to avoid restriction of movement (which is common in many of the Capricorn ailments) they must cultivate flexibility and tolerance and learn not to take themselves too seriously.

The parts of the body 'ruled' by Capricorn are the knees, bones, teeth, skin and the skeletal system. The native tends to suffer from sluggish circulation causing colds, rheumatism and arthritis. Neuralgia and dental troubles sometimes occur. The Capricornian tends to build up toxins which cause skin troubles and related ailments and, like Cancer, they can suffer from digestive troubles.

Nature Cure treatment will remove toxicity, with careful attention to diet. Reflexology to prevent inhibition of movement and osteopathy to treat specific illness of this nature are also beneficial.

As regards exercise, anything which helps to keep movement fluid is valuable. Swimming is excellent and competitive sports are usually enjoyed but football and related sports where joints can go out easily are best avoided.

For relaxation, the Capricornian needs massage, and deep-breathing exercises. Any creative activity which will release inhibition of emotion will be helpful. If the Capricornian can dance or act (even in the privacy of his own room) this will be a great release of tension. Relaxation needs to be fun – there is already enough serious purpose in the Capricornian's daily life.

Most dairy foods, yogurt, citrus fruits, nuts and bran should find a place in the Capricornian's diet. Like Cancer, he should never eat when upset. Sprouts of alfalfa are strengthening and weight adding and will help to prevent arthritis.

His tissue salt is Calcium Phosphate (*Calc. Phos.*) which helps to build bones and teeth and overcomes a deficiency of albumen. Tension will inhibit the absorbtion of this salt.

Among the homoeopathic remedies, Calendula tincture should be kept handy for accidents and for dental use. Aconitum 6 is useful for muscular pains caused by chills and *Nux. Vom.* 30 should be taken when applicable.

A great many herbs will be found useful to the Capricornian:

Bay is valuable for skin troubles.

Blackberry is good for psoriasis.

Chamomile can be used externally for neuralgia and toothache.

Cloves are a well-known remedy for toothache. The tea is warming and stimulating.

Camphor eases chills, rheumatic and neuralgia pains.

Chicory is a help for rheumatic conditions.

Comfrey strengthens bones and helps the skin.

Elderberry is a mild astringent for the skin and helps rheumatic conditions.

Feverfew should be taken regularly to prevent arthritis, if you suffer from cold hands and feet.

Mustard helps to prevent chills and eases rheumatic pains.

Pennyroyal is warming and makes a good tea for soothing teething infants.

Yerba Mate is also taken as a tea and is excellent for rheumatism.

Vervain is the Bach flower remedy which is likely to be appropriate for Capricornians, at times.

Psychologically, the Capricornian tends to be over-concerned with the material world. If he achieves power, he can find it a lonely position, and he needs to handle it wisely, if it is not to corrupt. If he does not achieve his aims, he can become embittered, and he needs to realise that this can, literally, poison him by releasing toxins into the blood stream. He may need to set his sights lower and be content with achieving a more domestic happiness.

However, there is no doubt that his main difficulty stems from the inability to release emotions. He appears to be scared of knowing his true nature and would probably shrink from exploring it, yet this is precisely what he needs to do, in order to realise his full potential. Feelings which are controlled to freezing point literally freeze the limbs, and tensions are often shown by the way that limbs are held tensely and, ultimately, movement becomes restricted. All this can be avoided if the Capricornian is willing to follow the hints given here.

Aquarius

The Sun is in this sign about 21 January to 18 February. The planet Uranus 'rules' Aquarius and if it, or the Moon, is in this sign at the time of birth you will also be an Aquarian type.

This will apply, as well, if Aquarius is on the Ascendant (rising) in your birth chart.

This is an Air sign, and in common with the others (Gemini and Libra) the Aquarian is interested in the world of ideas. The influence of Uranus is to make him inventive, so he is drawn to new or unusual subjects. He is usually extremely intelligent, though this is sometimes only apparent in his own special field.

In common with 'the Age of Aquarius', the native demands a great deal of personal freedom and is willing to go to revolutionary lengths to retain it. Unlike the Sagittarian, who took his freedom for granted, the Aquarian always feels that his is threatened and he is prepared to fight for it. Yet, he is also a great humanitarian and would like to see everyone sharing in the good things of life. In order to achieve this, it is necessary to give up some of one's personal freedom for the good of all, and here we have the dilemma of the Aquarian Age perfectly mirrored in the character of the typical Aquarian. No wonder that he is a restless person and with a great desire to change everything. He has a fascinating and dominating personality and he holds to his own opinions stubbornly, not caring if he is 'the only one in step'. His originality and inventiveness together with his freedom of thought may be well ahead of his own generation, so that he may appear rather 'cranky' to other people.

Like all the Air types, his emotions tend to be cool and feelings are expressed with difficulty. Such is his obsession for freedom that even his closest friends may feel that they do not really know him. He seems to think that revealing himself to others is an invasion of his privacy – like a rape of the essential self. On the surface, he is an extremely friendly person, very gregarious and always willing to help others. He often joins clubs and associations, especially those formed for humanitarian purposes.

He needs to have a certain amount of freedom in his career and is often attracted to scientific and inventive work. Many

Aquarians are found in the world of television, presenting their own programmes, reporting news or getting into some other niche where they can 'do their own thing', especially if this means breaking new ground.

Aquarians need marriage partners who are cool-natured like themselves, or one of the Fire signs who are very self-contained and not over dependant on the partner, emotionally. They will be loyal and faithful once a partnership is formed, but will not tolerate possessiveness in the partner.

In the days when astrologers thought that the planetary system only extended to Saturn, they gave this planet the rulership of Aquarius, and it is true that, with all his Uranian qualities of restlessness and desire for change, the native does combine the Saturnine qualities of caution and recognition of the need for discipline. It is this that stops many Aquarians from becoming passionate revolutionaries and limits their activities to an exchange of ideas on the subject. They also show the stubborn qualities of Saturn in maintaining their own opinions in the face of all opposition.

Where the need for discipline is not recognised, psychological difficulties often arise if the Aquarian is in confining conditions, as these are incompatible with his desire for freedom. He needs to learn to feel free within the limitations imposed by normal life.

Aquarius is also a Fixed sign, which again expresses the idea of control, but Fixed Air can stagnate and some Aquarians express this, being full of ideas which are never put into practice. In the best type, however, this manifests as 'controlled expression' as shown by the careers suggested.

Aquarians are always interested in new knowledge and are usually tolerant and open-minded so that they also make good researchers. They are very attracted to the unusual and theirs is said to be the sign of the Astrologers. They soak up knowledge and their power of concentration is formidable.

They can be completely unconventional and while this can be a valuable trait it can also lead the Aquarian into the pursuit of the 'way out' for its own sake. 'Free love' can become license without responsibility, which is a far cry from the Aquarian ideal of the freedom of brotherhood of all.

As his opposition, Leo ruled the heart, so Aquarius rules the circulatory system, and it also rules the shins and ankles. Aquarians tend to suffer from high blood-pressure, hardening of the arteries, varicose veins, swollen ankles and muscular cramp. Accidents are likely to affect the ankles, and sprains, in particular, are common.

With an interest in unusual things, the Aquarian often responds well to Radionics and will also accept healing of all kinds. For those who are still obsessed with the idea of freedom and who feel restricted, Encounter Groups may be helpful.

For exercise, the Aquarian needs something fairly strenuous and in the open air to help the circulation, cycling, skipping and so on, and for the same reason it is very important that he learns to breathe properly. This will oxygenate the blood and prevent it from being sluggish.

For relaxation, the mind needs to be stilled and yoga or something similar is indicated. Relaxing massage is also helpful. The Aquarian usually needs lots of sleep but often is unable to get it because his mind is so active. He should, therefore, avoid anything which is mentally stimulating late in the evening.

The Aquarian should include honey, lemon, apples and cheese in his diet.

His tissue salt is Sodium Chloride (*Nat. Mur.*) which balances the water content of the body, but the Cancer tissue salt, Fluoride of Lime is also indicated for varicose veins.

As regards homoeopathy, the most useful remedy is likely to be *Rhus. Tox.* tincture for sprains.

Among the herbal remedies, the following will be found useful:

Bergamot for relaxation. Both the tea and the pot pouri will help to cure insomnia.

Borage will cleanse the bloodstream and is useful for sprains. It is also a heart stimulant.

Caraway is also a strengthening agent for sprained limbs.

Dandelion cleanses the blood stream and is a tonic.

Hyssop regulates blood-pressure and will relieve bruising.

Nettle improves the circulation and is a blood purifier.

Rosemary reduces high blood-pressure and stimulates the circulation. This is a valuable herb for the Aquarian and should always be available.

Yerba Mate is useful as a stimulant when necessary.

One of the Bach flower remedies, Water Violet is likely to be appropriate for many Aquarians.

Psychologically, the Aquarian needs to recognise that he is subconsciously fearful of life itself. He is only willing to get involved on the surface. This results in some repression of the feelings and leads to difficulties in making deep relationships. In a sense, this is a denial of his own individuality. Even though the Aquarian may feel that his freedom is threatened by others, in truth he is not free to express himself fully because of this attitude, so he is really thwarting his own instincts which urge him to be his own man. A willingness to share himself with others at a deeper level gives the evolved native a deep satisfaction that is not achieved by most of his fellow Aquarians.

In order to be free, the Aquarian must recognise that he himself needs to break out of the confining conditions which hamper him. If he is truly his own man he will *feel* free and independent. It is his own fears which shackle him. Freedom of the spirit is the only true freedom.

Pisces

The Sun is in this sign from about 19 February to 19 March, but if Pisces is rising, or if the Moon or Neptune are in it at the time of your birth, you will probably have some of the Piscean characteristics.

This is a Water sign, so Pisceans are emotional and receptive, and their ruler, Neptune, adds a quality of intuition and elusiveness. With Neptune being the god of the sea, it is hardly surprising that Pisces is the most 'watery' of the signs, so that the native is very sensitive indeed. Pisceans are very adaptable (just as water takes the shape of its container). They have a great need to feel loved and like to get on with everyone, so they can tend to 'run with the hare and hunt with the hounds'. Being ultra-sensitive, they try to stay out of trouble as much as possible, so they have the elusive quality of being elsewhere when the storms break. Nevertheless, they are sympathetic and are always to be found helping and supporting other people in their troubles. Normally optimistic and happy people, they can become a prey to apprehensions – sometimes because they do sense coming events, but often because they tend to anticipate things which may never happen.

Their love life is usually happy, partly because they are so adaptable but also because they like to make other people happy and take pleasure in giving practical help as well as their own generous affection. They need the reassurance of love and appreciation and will become very unhappy if this is not forthcoming. They are good lovers but tend to idealise the loved one.

Pisceans are often found in careers like nursing where service is given and they tend to feel that their life is being wasted if they are not doing something for others. Ideas and inspiration are plentiful, but tend to lack shape, unless other parts of the birth chart show practicality.

Such sensitive and loving people are devastated by criticism and unkindness. They have a need for privacy as they can become mentally and emotionally drained by others. Their way of avoiding unpleasantness is to retreat or escape and for this reason some of them turn to drugs and alcohol. However, many of them, with their unique sensitivity, seem to realise this danger and will not touch either. In this, they are very wise as Pisceans are particularly prone to drug or alcohol poisoning – also to fish poisoning and to water which contains any impurities.

Pisceans are intelligent and inventive, but they tend to escape into a fantasy world and can spend too much time day-dreaming (or becoming TV addicts!). But although his inner life is the real life to the Piscean, many live richly and fully by following their own intuition and channelling it in constructive ways.

They have a unique sense of rhythm and can realise their fantasies as poetry, fiction-writing, dance-dramas, etc. Acting also appeals to them as they can then live in a make-believe world.

They are very susceptible to beauty and many Pisceans can create it, so careers in all the arts appeal to them, together with those that give service to others, and those connected with the sea.

The polarity with their opposite sign, Virgo, is shown in their adaptability and their desire to serve others. Both suffer with the stomach and intestines when upset or worried (and all the Water signs worry).

The old ruler of this sign was thought to be Jupiter and it is true that the Piscean has much in common with the Jupiterian sign, Sagittarius. Both are naturally cheerful and philosophical and both realise the value of detachment from the things of this world.

Pisceans will ignore difficulties as long as possible and then try to get round them or away from them – to get over the ground as lightly as possible is their aim. Their motto might be 'Anything for a quiet life'. They easily become over-anxious and fearful, and they can then be very secretive, making efforts to conceal things which they feel might attract criticism from others. Often other people are not interested at all, but the Piscean is taking no chances. Self-deception is common and so is the deliberate deception of others, if it will make life easier for them.

Many are mediumistic and almost all of them have a rich inner life. They recognise the essential unity of all life, even though its expressions are so varied and they often feel a sense of unity with all forms of life – hence their deep compassion for others.

In living so much inside their own heads and with their emotional natures, it is not surprising if some of them become confused with what is reality. Indeed, in one sense, their view of it may be more valid than the usually accepted view that reality is what is perceived physically.

Ideally, all Pisceans should live near water and in natural conditions.

The parts of the body ruled by Pisces are the duodenum, the feet, the pituitary and pineal glands and the lymphatic system. They suffer from glandular disorders, mucus in the lungs, conjunctivitis, duodenal troubles and foot disorders. They tend to be overweight, chiefly because they retain water. They also suffer from nervous stress and drug allergies.

For treatment, they are particularly sympathetic to healing and herbal treatment and to reflexology (except for foot troubles).

They need rhythmic exercise – dancing, swimming and eurythmy are particularly suitable.

They can relax easily, but meditation will usually be a way of life to them. Most Pisceans enjoy fishing and sailing.

They should include liver in their diet, as a good source of the iron they so badly need. Also cucumbers, almonds and melon.

Homoeopathic remedies should include *Arsen. Alb.* 6 for food poisoning and Ruta tincture for corns. Arsenicum 30 should be used for the times when they are feeling apprehensive, and Pulsatilla 30 can also be appropriate for the Piscean.

The tissue salt needed is Phosphate of Iron (*Ferr. Phos.*) to oxygenate the blood.

Among the herbs which are helpful to Pisceans are the following:

Kelp which is especially indicated as a good source of iron – as this is derived from seaweed it seems particularly applicable to Father Neptune's child.

Bilberry to counteract water retention.

Bergamot which is relaxant and sleep-inducing.

Arrowroot to calm the stomach.

Balm for its soothing properties and for digestive troubles.

Borage for its stimulating qualities and for courage.

Chicory to eliminate mucus.

Elderberry to induce sleep.

Eyebright for conjunctivitis.

Ginseng as a tonic for the nervous system.

Horseradish for glandular troubles.

Several Bach remedies may be helpful to the Piscean and the descriptions should be read to decide which is most applicable. These are Clematis, Mimulus, Cerato and Water Violet.

Psychologically, the Piscean is inclined to under rate himself and to be overconcerned with others. He needs to recognise this, as he tends to carry other people's burdens, like Cancer, and fear their criticism, like Scorpio (the other water signs). He should guard the privacy that he really needs in order to renew himself and to find the peace within, otherwise he is at the mercy of every harsh wind that blows and may decide to 'escape' into illness. He is the most impressionable of the zodiacal signs and can become a hypochondriac if life gets too much for him.

I would remind you that we all have a mixture of zodiacal signs emphasised in our birth charts, so it is unusual to find marked characteristics so strong that there is nothing to counteract them. It is for this reason that I have used the phrase 'tends to' all through this section.

I would also like to remind you that no one needs to be ill just because the constitution gives a tendency to a certain disease. Awareness of this and the following of a healthy regime is a better remedy than an apple to keep the doctor away.

The Zodiacal Types as Healers

It has been said that many people could transmit a form of healing – perhaps all of us – if we tried. One theory is that it is a faculty that was available to man and which has been lost through neglect – just as a muscle will atrophy, if not used.

Whether this is true or not, it is certain that each of the zodiacal types has something to contribute to the health of mankind. It is equally certain that we can all improve our own health and the birth chart gives important clues as to how to do this, as we have already seen.

We are not slaves to our physical makeup as indicated by our birth charts. I most strongly refute the idea that we are all conditioned by what the charts show and can do nothing to help ourselves.

The Arien, for instance, need not be dominated by the destructive Martian instincts, but can harness the vitality and drive by learning control. Such a person can make a fine surgeon (perhaps specialising in brain troubles) or a psychiatrist, but even on a more mundane level his positive outlook and personal courage can set a good example to the hypochondriacs of this world.

The other Fire signs, Leo and Sagittarius can also contribute the positive and optimistic spirit that helps so much to make people feel better – a powerful regenerator. In addition, Leo types often become interested (perhaps because of their love of drama and makeup) in beauty therapy and cosmetic surgery. Sagittarians sometimes find a niche in connection with sport – muscle building by weightlifting training or organising sports for the physically handicapped.

Taureans need to educate their fine palates to appreciate wholesome foods, rather than the rich and luxurious meals which they so much enjoy. Their interest in the subject makes them good dieticians, while the many who enjoy gardening can ensure that they get fresh fruit and vegetables. Taureans are also often attracted to herbalism. If a more direct career in medicine appeals, they might consider that of almoner.

Virgo and Capricorn, the other two Earth signs, are both practical types who are drawn to service to others. Virgo has particular feeling for natural foods and is also willing to take the trouble to search out the precise remedy required, so that homoeopathy is a likely career. Capricornians make good paediatricians (children's doctors) and some have skill in skingrafting. Dentistry and osteopathy both have an obvious connotation with this sign.

Geminians have operative hands and can use them in the service of the sick in many ways. Massage and reflexology are two obvious indications. If they will be bothered to do sick visiting, their cheerful chatter and wide interests can bring a real breath of fresh air to those in confined conditions. They also make good speech therapists.

The other Air signs of Libra and Aquarius are often found helping in the service of the sick. Librans, in particular, make fine diagnosticians as they have a feeling for what is out of balance and usually know how to adjust it. Aquarians can work well with the mentally sick, being humanitarian but detached.

Their skill in this field, however, is for medical research.

All the Water signs (Cancer, Scorpio and Pisces) are, as one would expect, very suggestible, and they ought to run a mile from anyone who is inclined to tell others that they have something wrong with them, or that they look ill and also from those who insist on describing their own symptoms in detail. When they recognise this trait in themselves and can control it, the Water signs are usually able to help others in a sympathetic, but bracing way and make good nurses and therapists, especially the Cancerians and Pisceans. The Scorpio native is more likely to be attracted to psychiatry and psychotherapy. All are excellent at using 'intuitive' techniques.

It is of course unlikely that all zodiacal types would be drawn to a career connected with health in preference to other callings, but the scope is so wide that all could find their niche, if they so wished.

THE WHOLE BIRTH CHART: A NOTE FOR ASTROLOGERS

Charts of Healers

The birth charts of intuitive healers, of all types, often seem to feature a Grand Trine in Water, or significant planets in that element. This, of course, would indicate the ease with which they work on an emotional/intuitive link. Virgo is often prominent and this is traditionally the sign connected with health and service and, of course, the use of the hands. Libra is another sign which often features prominently and this would appear to be connected with balance. After all, if someone is ill it is because something is out of balance and Libra, apparently, has the ability to put it right. This is also an intuitive sign though many astrologers seem to ignore the fact. Good intuitive healers need to be 'earthed' so expect to see an Earth sign prominent even if Virgo is not one of them.

What the Planets Tell Us

Each of the planets, in so far as they have rulership over various parts of the body, should be considered in assessing the health of the native. However, apart from the natal Sun and Moon, the most important ones are Mercury, Mars and Saturn.

Mercury is particularly important in showing the mental attitude of a patient and of the type of nervous system with which we are dealing. The obviously 'nervy' types – the Air signs – can vary from Gemini (always on the go) to Libra (apprehensive of anything unpleasant) and Aquarius who tends to worry over health difficulties. The Mercury-ruled Virgoan may be a victim of his own fussiness and strain the nervous system by trying to accomplish too much. But even the more stolid Mercury in Capricorn, while not stressing the nervous system, will indicate the attitude of mind towards health, and this will tend to be in the form of suppression of symptoms – a reluctance to acknowledge that they are there. Thus Capricornians often neglect their health and are reluctant to seek treatment. The Fire signs tend to ignore it for another reason. They want to get on with life and will tell you that they 'can't afford to be ill'. The Water signs can be the most sensible in seeking early help for disorder, though they can easily become too obsessed with their health.

Mars, of course, indicates the vitality and here the position in the birth chart seems to be as important as the zodiacal sign. To express his principle fully, Mars ought to be 'out in the world' and if he is near the IC, the vitality may fluctuate considerably, especially if he is also receiving stressful aspects from other planets. A well-aspected Mars in the sixth house usually ensures plenty of vitality.

Stressful aspects between Mercury and Mars will incline the subject to be accident prone. These people can also be reckless drivers and would do well to decide not to drive themselves. The aspect implies an impairment in judgement or sheer thoughtlessness. Mars also correlates with fever and its good application is to burn up impurities.

Saturn imposes limitations and it is not always possible to tell from a birth chart whether these will be limitations to health, but they are likely to be so if this planet is making stressful aspects to the Sun or Mars, or is in the third house of movement or the sixth house of health. Difficult aspects to Mercury, Moon or Venus may indicate depression, with due respect to the houses tenanted. Inferiority complexes are afflictions of a Saturnine nature and these are sometimes triggers for psychosomatic illness.

I have found the quincunx to be more stressful than the square while oppositions often seem to work quite well in health conditions.

Other Considerations

It hardly needs saying that there is no method by which one can tell whether a difficult aspect will apply to the health of the native rather than to any other aspect of his life. Charts of quite severely handicapped people will be exactly the same as those of their astrological twins, even though the others may be quite healthy and may experience their difficult aspects in totally different ways.

An astrologer who has access to the charts of the parents will be able to deduce the kind of upbringing the child has had, and may also see where hereditary traits are likely to occur.

The Moon sign often shows the type of life decision a person has made as a result of their childhood upbringing. For instance, I once remarked in a lecture that I had met several people with Moon in Cancer who had decided at an early age

THE WHOLE BIRTH CHART

that they must look after themselves, since they had formed the opinion that their parents would not do so. In the lecture hall were five people who had this placing and four of them agreed that this also applied to them. Most of them had become children of broken marriages or had lost a parent shortly after making the decision. Where childhood decisions have been carried into adult life and are no longer applicable, there will be psychological difficulties which may exteriorise as illness.

Great care is necessary when dealing with any such illness, as the cure may be worse than the disease from the patient's point of view. A change in life-style may be too painful to contemplate, and the decisions and feelings of the patient should always be respected.

A woman who was agoraphobic became aware, through counselling based on her birth chart, that she was using her phobia as a protection against her own sexual feelings. Her husband did not satisfy her, either as lover or partner. She came to realise that she did not regard him as a man, but as another of her children. As an agoraphobic she could cope, in the privacy of her home, with looking after all her children (including her husband) and she ran no risk of meeting other men and having extra-marital affairs.

Her first instinct after she had faced the truth about the situation was to continue with psychotherapy and emerge as a whole person. But second thoughts prevailed and her ultimate decision was that she would keep her marriage intact for the sake of everyone concerned – and remain an agoraphobic if that was the necessary condition.

It is, of course, extremely important, that we should not be too rigid over the interpretation of charts. Having said that most illnesses which include restriction of movement will show up in Earth signs, I set up a chart for a lady who had an artificial hip. The chart showed no planets in Earth and not much in Fixed signs, but Mars – the vitality – was in the sixth house of health in square to Pluto in the sign of Sagittarius, which rules 'long journeys' and the hips and thighs.

Most often, it is the psychological difficulties, together with the life style of the native which predisposes him to certain ailments.

With all this information, the best way in which an astrologer can help patients is firstly, to make them aware of how they themselves contribute to their own illnesses and secondly, to forecast by means of progressions and transits the likely periods when health will be threatened, so that special precautions can be taken in good time. These may range from merely taking a holiday (if the prime cause – the trigger – is likely to be overwork) to finding a new interest or even embarking on a course of Nature Cure to detoxify the system.

I am very much against astrologers putting negative thoughts into patients' minds by specifying that they have a named illness (we all have cancerous cells – we don't all – or even most of us – get cancer). Let us keep our rightful role of encouraging people to realise their full potential and to do all they possibly can to keep themselves healthy, and leave the treatment of chronic or acute illness to the experts.

FURTHER INFORMATION

Organisations offering multiple therapies
The Institute for Complementary Medicine
4 Tavern Quay, Plough Way, Surrey Quays, London SE16 1QZ.
Phone 071–237–5165.

Will supply details of homoeopaths, osteopaths, accupuncturists, etc. Local libraries may also have details of the Institute's Public Information Point in your area.

The Cancer Help Centre
Grove House, Cornwallis Grove, Clifton, Bristol BS8 4PG. Phone 0272–743–216.

Offers healing, diet advice, counselling, meditation, art and music therapy, etc. Day courses and residential care. They will also know if there is a local centre in your area.

Blackthorn Trust Medical Centre
475 Tonbridge Road, Maidstone, Kent ME16 9LH. Phone 0622–72-6128.

Offers natural medicaments, counselling, eurhythmy and artistic therapies. Treatment offered regardless of financial means.

Marylebone Health Centre
St Marylebone Parish Church, 17 St Marylebone Road, London NW1 5LT.
See page 73 for details.

Glyncorrwg Health Centre
Waun Avenue, Glyncorrwg, Port Talbot, S. Wales SA13 3DP
Holistic Health Centre.

Aromatherapy
International Federation of Aromatherapists
4 Eastmearn Road, London SE21 8HA.
Books: *The Art of Aromatherapy* by Robert Tisserand (C. W. Daniel).
The Joy of Aromatherapy by Cathy Hopkins (Angus & Robertson).

Astrology
Book: *The Art of Astrology* by Sheila Geddes (Aquarian Press).

Self-Development with Astrology by Sheila Geddes (Foulsham).
Prediction monthly magazine. Contains adverts from astrologers, schools, etc.

Colour Healing
Mrs Alice Howard, 7 Riffel Road, Willesden Green, London NW2 4NY.

Diet
Book, *The Food Pharmacy* by Jean Carper (Positive Paperbacks).

Healing
Confederation of Healing Organisations
Suite J, The Red and White House, 133 High Street, Berkhamsted, Herts HP4 2DJ. Phone 0442–870–667.

Herbs
National Institute of Medical Herbalists
9 Palace Gate, Exeter EX1 1JA. Phone: 0392–426022.
Suppliers: All branches of Culpepers.

Homoeopathy
Suppliers: Ainsworth's Homoeopathic Pharmacy, 38 New Cavendish Street, London W1M 7LH. Phone 071–935–5330.

Kinesiology
Brian H. Butler BA, LCSP (Phys), MBEOA, 39 Browns Road, Surbiton, Surrey KT5 8ST. Phone 081–399–3215.

Massage
Massage Course Information:
The Churchill Centre
22 Montague Street, London W1. Phone 071–402–9475.
Book: *The Massage Book* by George Downing (Arkana).

Radionics
The Radionic Association
Baerlein House, Goose Green, Deddington, Oxon. OX15 0SZ.

Reflexology
Association of Reflexologists
27 Old Gloucester Street, London, WC1N 3XX

Index

Medical Index

To enable you to find the particular therapy that interests you, the following short index will prove useful.

Astrological Index

Signs of the zodiac – health problems, health solutions.